THE WOOD
FROM THE TREES

by

RICHARD JEFFERIES

LONDON:
THE PILOT PRESS LTD.

First published in March 1945 *by*
The Pilot Press Ltd.,
45 *Great Russell St., London, W.C.*1

BOOK
PRODUCTION
WAR ECONOMY
STANDARD

This book is produced in complete
conformity with the authorised
economy standards

PRINTED IN GREAT BRITAIN
AT THE CHISWICK PRESS
NEW SOUTHGATE, LONDON

CONTENTS

*

LIST OF ILLUSTRATIONS

*

THE WOOD FROM THE TREES

> "Since it is certain and demonstrable that all arts and artisans whatsoever, must fail and cease, if there were no timber and wood in a nation (for he that shall take his pen, and begin to set down what art, mystery, or trade belonging any way to human life, could be maintain'd and exercis'd without wood, will quickly find that I speak no paradox) I say, when this shall be well consider'd, it will appear, that we had better be without gold than without timber: This contemplation, and the universal use of that precious material (which yet is not of universal use 'till it be duly prepar'd) has mov'd me to design a solemn chapter for the seasoning, as well as to mention some farther particular application of it."
>
> JOHN EVELYN: *Sylva*

INTRODUCTION

SINCE JOHN EVELYN wrote *Sylva* in the seventeenth century, no one has attempted to bring up to date the history of timber and forestry and to make an assessment of their importance to modern industrial societies. It is remarkable that this vital branch of human activity has escaped the notice of all for so long.

The short review which follows does not in any way claim to be a comprehensive study of the whole subject. What I have tried to do is to gather together something of the story of wood and trees with particular stress upon the importance that timber has assumed in the terrific struggle of war.

The war will have induced unpredictable changes in all our ways, both social and industrial, and I believe that as a raw material of industry of the future, timber in one form or another is destined to play an ever developing part When the technical advances which have been achieved are made known and become fully understood by industry, peace time living will be enlivened by the new variety which timber products can endow in many spheres of activity.

The greatest need is for some general knowledge of all the new things that industry can provide to meet our daily wants; and perhaps what follows will act as a groundwork in the study of one of the most useful and romantic of Nature's products.

"Is it not after all this to be deplor'd, that we who have such perpetual use and convenience for ship-timber, should be driven to procure it of foreign stores, so many thousand loads, at intolerable prices: But this we are oblig'd to do and supply from the Eastern countries, as far as Norway, Poland, Prussia, Dantzick, and farther, even from Bohemia, tho' greatly impair'd by sobbing so long in the passage."

JOHN EVELYN: *Sylva*

CHAPTER I

THE TIMBERS OF PEACE

THE TREES of the forests have from the earliest days provided man with a useful and easily-worked raw material for shelter, for tools and in building boats to sail the seas and rivers in search of fish or riches. From the days of the simple demands of primitive man, timber in a variety of different forms has been a standby in the development of many human activities. The early bows were made from the sturdy yew trees, spears had wooden shafts, men went to fish or to fight in wooden boats or canoes, and the homes of the men and women who had emerged from the caves of the stone age were made from the tree trunks and boughs of the local forests. Later on, wood became one of the most important materials for keeping man warm, and continued to serve as fuel even after the discoveries of coal and oil. In countless instances over the long trail of history, timber has contributed to a vital jump forward in human development; or has aided the establishment of the supremacy of a particular race or state.

In peace and in war, wood has been one of the most useful servants of mankind. When the soil was tilled, a sharpened stake was the first plough; the problem of land transport was solved with the invention of the wheel, in its humblest form merely a transverse section of a tree. As the human race grew up, wood became more, not less, important to its development and an essential part of organised life. All the great maritime races of the past have depended upon plentiful supplies of timber for the construction of their boats and ships which in their very infancy were but tree trunks hollowed out. From these small beginnings came the fleets of the ancient empires, down the path of history to the victorious modern battle fleets of Nelson. Rollo, the red-headed Viking,

set out in his high-prowed boats made from pine to the conquest of the
Normandy coast; Columbus discovered the West Indies and first saw
its sand and rock from the deck of a timber ship. Vasco da Gama circled
the cape and braved the southern storms with sturdy wood beneath his
feet. About two thousand years before the Genoese sailor set out for
the New World or the Portuguese adventurer circumnavigated Africa,
the Phœnicians of Carthage sailed their inland sea in the boats they had
constructed from the sad cedars of Lebanon, trading and conquering
from the coasts of Syria to the shores of Spain. Their supremacy, like
that of many great peoples to follow them, was in no small way due to
their sea power, and this power had its roots in their skill at building
ships from the mighty trees of their homelands.

The most lasting monument to timber's usefulness to man is
undoubtedly in architecture where, from early days, wood has been one
of the foremost materials not only to provide the shelter but also to
embellish the interior, a use which has persisted down to this day. Even
as late as Saxon times, the houses of the well-to-do were built entirely
of timber, but it was not until the middle ages that it came into its own
in domestic and church architecture. There are few more fitting tributes
to the beauty and durability of timber than the Gothic woodcarving of
the monasteries and churches built over 800 years ago, for the medieval
monks were masters of their craft and painstaking in the extreme, so
that a lifetime was not too long to spend on some carved screen or
timbered roof. The shrine of Edward the Confessor in Westminster
Abbey still stands sound after eight centuries, and the stalls in Winchester
Cathedral are miracles of intricate carving and a priceless heritage of the
skill of the craftsmen in wood. The dark oak floors, beamed roofs and
massive wooden chests of the medieval architectural style gave way to
the more domestic effects of the late fourteenth and early fifteenth century
ideas of interior decoration when long galleries of panelled walls, elegant
staircases and all-timber floors made the homes of the great English
families treasures for all time. Haddon Hall in Derbyshire is a good
example of this kind of work, and it is said that the entire floor and
steps leading to the gallery were made from a single mighty oak which
once grew in the grounds of the estate. Later, the half-timbered house
with weathered oak beams and white plaster became fashionable, and
some striking examples of this relatively simple style can be seen in the
border villages and Chester, and at one time there were a few in the
city of Coventry.

In the houses themselves, new pieces of furniture were being added
and these were always of wood, such as old flaunders chests in dark oak
or the later beauties of workmanship associated with the names of
Sheraton and Chippendale. These are the glimpses into the past that
are remembered, but throughout the ages timber was being used in the
household as furniture or joinery right up until the present day when,
despite the introduction of so many alternatives, by far the greater part

of all household furniture and fittings is the product of the tree in one form or another; the form has changed considerably but the substance remains the same.

The nineteenth century witnessed the birth of the massive industrial demand for timber—a demand which has gone on increasing up to the present day. The uses to which this timber was put are touched upon in a later chapter, but in any event the whole list is too multifarious to give in detail. The important point is that the needs which emerged as a result of the industrial revolution were far and away too big to be met from the meagre resources of this country and the age of importation had begun. This development brought to Great Britain the timbers of practically every exporting country in the world and made her the largest importer of wood on earth.

*   *   *   *   *   *

To understand where the various types of timber come from and why Britain needs these numerous species necessitates a little knowledge of the tree geography of the world. Trees can be classed for simplification into two categories—coniferous and broad leaved, and this classification corresponds to the normal trade division of timbers into "softwoods" and "hardwoods". The division is not by any means ideal and can lead to considerable confusion, particularly as some so-called "softwoods" are very much harder in the ordinary sense of the term than many of the timbers classified as "hardwoods". The softest and lightest of all woods is a timber called balsa—which is actually a hardwood! In usage, the softwoods—which are by far the bigger group—are the timbers of construction and general use, whilst hardwoods, usually heavier in weight and more beautiful to the eye, are the timbers of decoration and most of those special purposes demanding great strength and durability. But again these two classifications are not by any means exclusive, for it is indeed difficult to give two clear definitions which will satisfy all considerations. Softwoods are from trees such as pines, firs and spruces, and hardwoods from oaks, elms, beeches, sycamore and mahogany—to mention but a very few of hundreds of different species.

The earth's surface is very liberally covered with trees of both categories, and it is not easy to tie particular species down as indigenous to particular climatic conditions. As a very rough and ready division, however, it can be said that softwoods grow in the main in the cold and temperate zones and hardwoods in the temperate and tropical zones. The biggest stands of softwood timber are in North Europe, Asia and North America; the biggest hardwood areas are in the centre of North America, the tropical areas of Africa, South America, Central and Southern Europe, India, Burma and parts of the East Indies. Here again the areas are not all-embracing since substantial quantities of timber are to be found in Australasia, the Pacific Islands and scattered

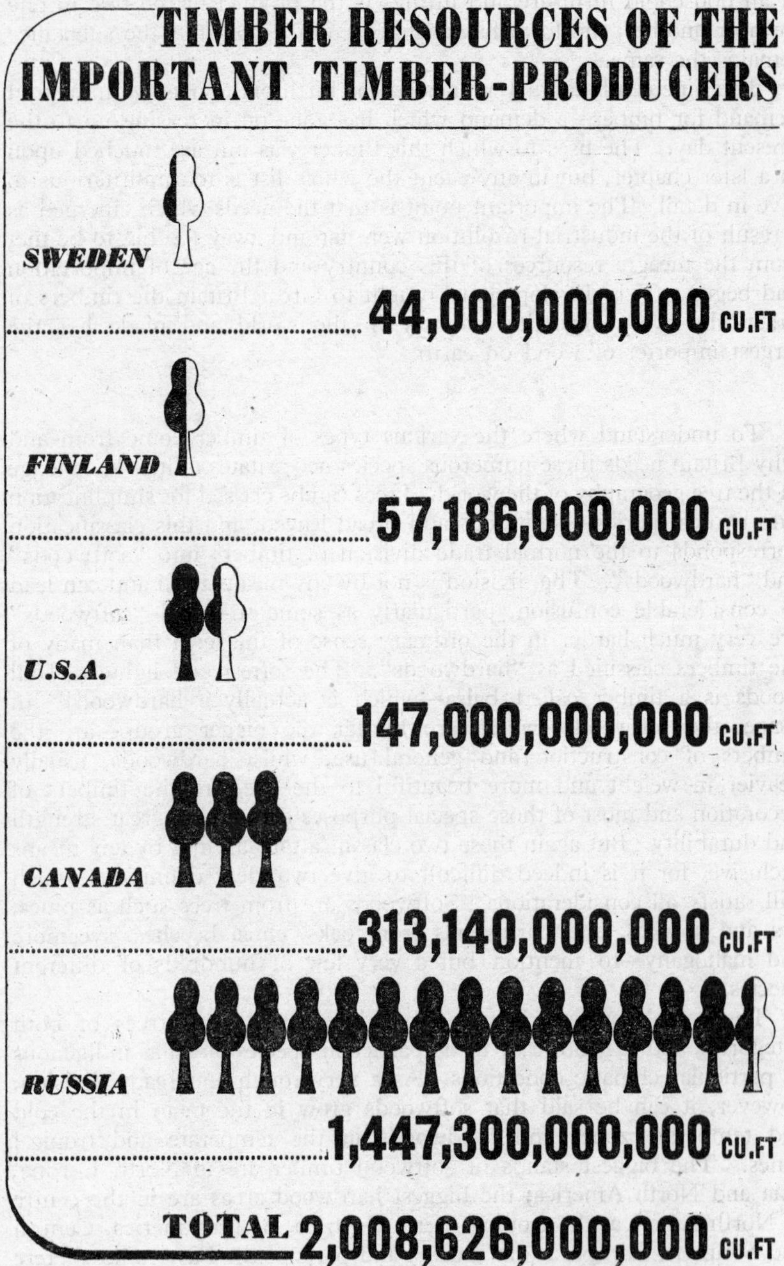

TIMBER RESOURCES OF THE IMPORTANT TIMBER-PRODUCERS

SWEDEN

44,000,000,000 CU.FT

FINLAND

57,186,000,000 CU.FT

U.S.A.

147,000,000,000 CU.FT

CANADA

313,140,000,000 CU.FT

RUSSIA

1,447,300,000,000 CU.FT

TOTAL 2,008,626,000,000 CU.FT

The above are the main producers at present exporting to world markets. Others have extensive treed areas not yet fully exploited, as for example Brazil.

over the tropical and sub-tropical areas of the world, but much of this timber is unsuitable for commercial exploitation either because of its quality and nature or because inaccessibility renders its production uneconomic under present conditions. It is not correct to say that it is "useless", since the ever changing industrial demand may well discover valuable uses for some of it, or find methods of overcoming the particular transport difficulties associated with its production. The vast majority of the world's timber resources are natural, that is to say they have not been consciously planted but are a gift from nature. Today it has become practicable with the increase in the knowledge of silviculture generally to start to grow the right kinds of trees not only to suit the soil and climate, but also for the industrial demands of the nations. No longer is it necessary to depend upon the vagaries of nature for the timber that is required, for it is now possible, at least in theory, to grow the softwoods that are most needed for constructional work near to the areas where the main demand exists. Naturally such a planned production has definite limits, since it is not practicable to plant exotic hardwood timbers in the tundra areas, nor to expect pines and firs to thrive on the Equator, and there are many areas of the earth's surface where no trees whatsoever can be induced to grow.

Anyone who tries to understand the figures of international timber trade will at once be fogged by the intricacies of the various kinds of unit employed by different countries in their method of calculating timber quantities. In this country, the normal unit for all kinds of softwoods is the "standard", which was originally a Russian measure known as the St. Petersburg or Petrograd standard, and was the cubical contents of 120 pieces of timber twelve feet long by eleven inches wide by one and half inches thick—a total of 165 cubic feet. To this day, the St. Petersburg standard is always used for calculating softwoods by all countries exporting to the British market, whilst hardwoods are usually reckoned merely in cubic feet. On the Continent, it was becoming more usual before the war to use the metric system and both hard and softwoods were calculated in cubic metres, but in spite of the greater convenience of this method it was not widely adopted in this country. In addition to these ordinary standards, there are special measures for particular types of timber, and indeed the whole business is quite unnecessarily complicated and some codification is long overdue. Cords, fathoms, Hoppus measure, board measure, string measure and the koku are but a few of the methods of measurement and units employed in various parts of the world to assess the quantity in a board, log or pile of timber. Throughout the North American Continent, the "board foot" is the standard of measurement for both hard and softwood. This board foot is one superficial foot of timber, one inch in thickness (i.e., one inch by twelve inches by twelve inches) or one twelfth of a cubic foot. Thus a square log twelve inches by twelve inches by twenty-four feet long contains 288 board feet or twenty-four cubic feet.

Britain's imports of timber in peace time required from ten to eighteen million tons of shipping to bring them to this country, and arrived across the seven seas from all corners of the earth. In practically every timber producing country, the British market was the most important, and Empire sources were becoming increasingly active as suppliers of this vast demand. The main sources of this supply have changed from decade to decade, and no one can say where the U.K. will draw the bulk of its needs after the war. In 1937, taken as an average year, the main exporters to Britain for all types of wood were Russia, Finland, Canada, the Scandinavian countries, the United States, Poland and Yugoslavia, with a large number of other countries supplying the relatively small quantities of hardwoods. The teak of Burma, Siam and Java, the exotic woods from India, the Andaman Islands and parts of Africa; the mahoganies from Nigeria and other parts of the West Coast of Africa, the special types of hardwoods from the Central American States and the Philippines—from far and wide the ships of commerce brought an immense variety of timbers to meet the almost fastidious demand of the British industrialists and consumers. Even Japan sent oak to the furniture makers of the East End of London, and it was indeed a remarkable fact that producers could afford to send their merchandise across the world into the small shop of some cabinet-maker in Stepney or Manchester, and that the consumer could pay the price demanded. The hundreds of shiploads of timber from the British Columbian forests, among the best ordinary softwoods in the world, made the journey through Puget Sound down the long coast of West America, through the Panama Canal and across the Atlantic to discharge in London, Liverpool, Hull, Cardiff, Newcastle or the Clyde. Every day the ships were arriving, sometimes with their decks covered in planks of timber piled almost up to the bridge. When the trader settled for these Canadian goods with his bank in London, of every £1 he paid, 10s. would go to the shipping companies in freight charges. It was a bulky, difficult cargo, liable to shift during transit and become a menace to the safety of the ship, for many of these ships carried grain from Canada below decks and timber on the decks.

From the Soviet Union and the Baltic countries of Norway, Sweden, Finland, Latvia, Lithuania and Poland (through Danzig and Gdynia) other cargoes were arriving, although their journey was not such a long and romantic one. Before Leningrad earned the respect and fame of the civilised world for its defence against the forces of Hitlerism, it was a household word in timber circles as one of the homes of the timber trade. The new Soviet Government had made Leningrad one of the most efficient and up-to-date timber ports in the world, with cranes that loaded more into a ship in one hour than had been loaded by hand in a day before the last war. Most of these Baltic ports were closed for six months of the year because of ice, and the shipping season commenced in June, so that into the next few months were packed all the energies of a season's sawmilling activities of the Soviet Union. Leningrad was not, of course, the only Russian port of shipment, for in the far north, the White Sea port of Archangel is world renowned as the shipping source of some of the finest of the world's softwoods. Timber from Archangel was the hall mark of quality and, although Leningrad had no equal as a shipping port, Archangel has always been a traditional centre of the trade.

These are the main shipping centres of the Soviet Union's vast production of wood goods of all kinds, for Russia has the biggest timber resources of any country in the world. About one-third of the world's timber areas are found on Russian soil, and there more than three-quarters of the trees grown are of the coniferous variety, so that the production of high grade softwood timbers is the main timber preoccupation of the Soviet Union in peace time. Many other producing countries are obliged to cut their full annual potential and some even exceed this increment, so that from year to year, despite their afforestation laws, they are becoming poorer and poorer in timber. But the Soviet Union seldom fells more than about half her annual increment, and is thus able to build up an enormous reserve of standing timber which will probably play an important part in the timber economics of the post-war period. In the Czarist days many of the mills were situated in the central parts of Russia, but the Soviet Union has established its biggest sawmills near to the sources of raw material in order to save unnecessary transportation. It is possible that as a result of this policy few have been destroyed by the Germans in the big advances, although those around Leningrad and on the Finnish frontier are certain to have suffered severely.

In the Russian mills every kind of timber product ranging from ordinary solid timber to pulpwood and plywood has been made and the total output continues to increase, or did so before the German attack upon the Soviet Union. The Soviets have spent large sums of money on bringing the equipment of the mills up-to-date and in giving all branches of the industry the latest machinery available to other producers. A great deal of this plant was actually made in the Soviet Union, and the degree of mechanisation both for converting and handling the timber is probably the highest of any producing country, with the possible exception of British Columbia. Piling elevators, shore and floating cranes, electrically driven motor-wagons and specialised lifting gear have cut production costs and enabled a speeding up of output which has been aided by the workers of the Stakhanov movement. Between 1935 and 1936 alone, the carrying capacity of an ordinary timber porter was increased by some thirty per cent. and in the latter year there were more than three thousand tractors used by the whole of the industry. Every device at the disposal of the ingenious Russian engineer has been brought into play to aid production, and the result is that before the present war Russia was producing three times as much timber as the old pre-1917 Russia could muster. Of this very much greater total, Russia exports only a small percentage, since in the building up of the new industrial state under the Five Year Plans the domestic demand has been sufficient to keep the majority of the mills busy without having to enter into the export markets. The export of timber and plywood is nevertheless one of the vital activities of Russian foreign trade, and the Soviets have always been very ready to fall in with any European or world schemes for the regulation of prices and the economic division of markets in order to stabilise international trading conditions.

Although her pre-war industry was on so extensive a scale, the full exploitation of Russia's immense forest areas has by no means been reached. In Siberia, for example, there are still vast areas which will not be opened up to the axe and sawmill until it is possible to provide better transport facilities in the form of roads and railways. In these areas grow thousand upon thousand of trees of good size and value which will one day provide many standards of timber for the peaceful development of Europe. The high quality of the Russian productions has already been mentioned, and this is a combination of the excellent type of raw material available and the traditional skill of the Russian workman as a timber operative. A certain amount of prejudice hindered the growth of the trading in timber between this country and Russia before the present war, and the desire to shelter and encourage Empire producers led to the preference on Canadian timber arranged at the Ottawa Conference; yet Russia is one of the natural purchasing countries for the United Kingdom, and it will be wise economic statesmanship after the war to zone the world's timber exporters so that Britain buys in those markets which are nearest to her shores. In any event the Soviet Union must continue to be one of the main exporters to the Continent of Europe where for nearly one hundred years she has sent her ships loaded to the decks with the softwoods of her northern territories.

Dotted along the Baltic both north and south were many other ports of less importance from which the timber of Baltic countries generally emerged into the markets of Europe and the United Kingdom. An exporting country of almost equal importance to the Soviet Union was Finland, carved out from some of the best timber producing country of old Imperial Russia. Many Finnish governments have contributed to the making of the timber industry of Finland one of the most progressive in the world, and with characteristic thoroughness, the Finns have built up a demand in this country for their products which rivalled, and in some years exceeded, that of the Russians. To the Finns, the British market, absorbing nearly two-thirds of their total export production, was the most important, and they had been among the pioneers in the orderly organisation of afforestation and forestry operations. This was necessary to maintain their existence because to them the growing tree was the main basis of the prosperity of their country and its four million people. In most years, Finland's total export of sawn softwoods to this country was in excess of that of the Russians, and this trade, which had grown yearly ever since Finland became an independent State, was one of the reasons for the strong friendship which existed between Britain and Finland, a friendship which many would like to see restored when the present unhappy choice of the Finns has been forgotten. For the Finn was a faithful, honest trader, able to strike a hard bargain but adhering to a promise given, and regarding the exploitation and development of his forests as a science in which he was determined to succeed. Many other countries have copied the afforestation laws which the Finns were among the first to impose, and as a result of this foresight, their beautiful land of lakes and forests should once again provide a sound livelihood to its people for many years to come.

The Baltic had been for so long the home of the Continental timber industry that a few important places are almost household words to many Englishmen. The port of Danzig, one of the towns of the old Hanseatic League, strove to emulate some of its fourteenth century fame and prosperity as a centre of Baltic trading activity when it became a busy timber shipping port. Its modern prosperity dated from the end of the last war when it arose again as the main port of shipment for merchandise from East Prussia and Poland. Poland possessed considerable rights in the Free City of Danzig and, although she was at the same time developing Gdynia as her main "national" outlet to the sea, for a long time the valuable communications of Danzig gave it a pre-eminence that other places could never fully enjoy. Its harbour facilities are excellent, with docks and wharves capable of berthing large ocean-going steamers and modern loading equipment which the Poles did much to instal and maintain. The timber community was drawn from all branches of Continental life and the atmosphere cosmopolitan. The fact that the Free City became a haven for large numbers of refugees, mostly with Nansen passports, added to the bizarre nature of business life there.

After the Russian Revolution in 1917, many traders in timber who wished to carry on their business under conditions of economic freedom and had no sympathy with the new era of Soviet planning, fled to Danzig and pursued a precarious living amid its ancient buildings. To join them came large numbers of Jews from Eastern Europe, who had either been forced out by their respective Governments or could sense the anti-Semitic storms brewing in the South and West and preferred to get out while the going was good. Many of these people found for the time being that the protection of the white paper or Nansen passport in fact gave them greater freedom of movement than most of the nationals of the countries they had left behind. They created a unique band of gregarious competitors, thriving on the café gossip that makes a "market" in some Continental centres. Some arrived in Danzig with a few miserable possessions tied to their backs and with no shoes to their feet, but by dint of their exceptional ability as traders, rather than producers, they built up businesses which in many cases made these

2

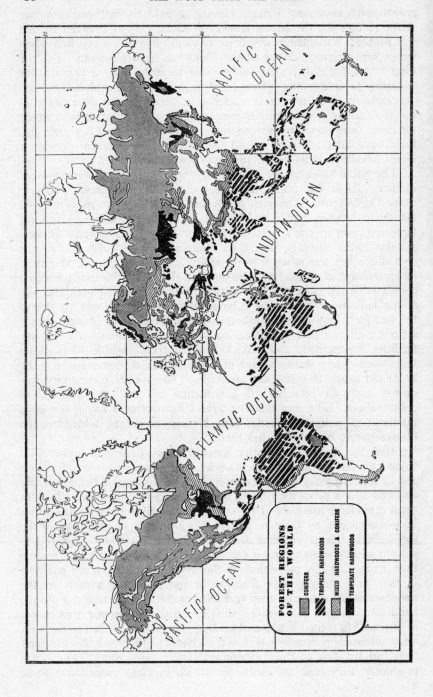

FOREST REGIONS
OF THE WORLD

CONIFERS

TROPICAL HARDWOODS

MIXED HARDWOODS & CONIFERS

TEMPERATE HARDWOODS

stateless citizens of the Free City wealthy men. Of course, in time the Nazis arrived to send most of them on yet another trek across Europe in search of somewhere to earn their living in the manner they preferred most; many never survived this second uprooting and languish today in obscure labour camps or enjoy the hard pleasures of the New Order in Europe, again with no shoes to their feet and weals across their once sturdy backs.

Danzig became the nerve centre of the central European timber trade and was particularly associated with the Polish industry. Several English firms set up their own offices there in order to be more closely in touch with this important market. The nature of the trading in the Free City often created a bad impression on the visiting business men, and since it was so closely connected with the Polish timber marketing, some of this stigma tended to attach itself to the Poles in their trading relations with this country. There were, to be sure, a number of wayward traders who had no capital or stocks but contrived to earn a few per cent profit by selling or buying across a café table, and it was these men who made the business reputation of Danzig a little unsavoury since they would either repudiate or disappear if the "bargain" went against them. But in spite of these difficulties, year by year an enormous quantity of timber left the port of Danzig for the British market. Softwoods and hardwoods, plywoods and veneers were shipped from there and Danzig began to flourish, although it was a precarious kind of existence. There are many stories to be told of the merchants who never carried out their contracts, of bargains that cost the British bargain hunters dear, of ingenious swindles that succeeded by the very audacity of their conception, and yet the other side of the medal shows a prosperous port supplying part of the vast needs of the British market and bringing cheap timber to other consumers who needed it in the development of their national economy. Through the port of Danzig went most of the timber exported to this country from Poland, Rumania and Czechoslovakia.

The Baltic countries of Estonia, Latvia and Lithuania all ranked as timber exporters and their natural market was Great Britain. Although they are small countries, their industries were well organised, particularly in the case of Estonia where Government agencies had by 1937 taken over the control of all forest exploitation, and were beginning in addition to create a small-scale but important cellulose production. Similar Government control existed in Latvia before the war, and there too pulpwood and cellulose production had been fostered by the State and had grown into a useful part of Latvia's economy. Before 1917 these three states were, of course, part of the old Imperial Russia and provided her with a considerable part of her total timber output. In the years before the present war, together they sent to this country a quantity of timber equal to nearly half of the total Soviet export to Britain, which gives some idea of their relative importance.

Poland, too, was the scene of an interesting experiment in State enterprise and was developing her industry to a high degree of efficiency. Early in the thirties the Government decided to take a direct interest in timber production and set up their own sawmills and marketing organisation. They began to ship timber of good quality and, although their costs and therefore their prices were proportionally high, they managed to create and maintain such an excellent reputation for reliability that their products found a ready sale in all the main markets, the most important of which was the United Kingdom. By 1938, the Government sawmills were responsible for more than half the total export of timber from Poland, and their venture had done much to make good their name as serious traders. The State Forests headquarters in Warsaw had little of the traditional "civil service" air about them; in fact the layout was more reminiscent of the offices of a successful joint stock company in London or New York than of the centre of a State trading department. The Poles had begun to build up a plywood manufacturing industry of some size, and they were suppliers of aircraft plywoods to the rapidly growing German airplane industry. A great deal of that plywood came roaring back to Poland in September, 1939.

Sweden and Norway were among the earliest and most faithful suppliers to Britain and their products have always been of the highest quality. The total quantity exported by Sweden was large, and in some years rivalled that of the Soviet Union. Of this total, Britain in normal times took about fifty per cent. and the rest went to all the main European markets, the most important of these being Germany, Denmark and France. With both the Scandinavian countries, Britain's trading relationship was always a very happy one, and this pleasant and profitable friendship was only broken by the present war.

The forests of the Scandinavian countries are to a certain extent the home of the world timber trade. They were lands of extensive coniferous forests, carpeting the sides of the mountains and giving to the countryside a simple beauty which provided a fitting background for the sturdy people who made their livelihood from the trees in the North. Pine trees and snow are the homes of these independent Nordics who have shown Hitler what they think of his twentieth century nonsense. The closer relations which are bound to exist after the war between Britain and the Scandinavian countries should mean an extension of trade in both directions. Incidentally, it is from Sweden that many sawmillers in this country have learnt much of what they know about production, for the machinery and methods of the Swedes are among the best and most efficient in the world. Swedish saws and mills are well known over here, and although their general methods of production are naturally different from the British, Swedish forestry practice has been the text-book of many branches of timber production.

Anyone who studies the annual trade figures may wonder why France appears to have so large a place amongst the exporters to Britain.

There are two reasons for this. The first is that for many years before the war France had been supplying quantities of pit props from her western forest lands to the coal mines of South Wales, and this export accounted for about one half of the total value of timber sent. The other reason is that from her West African colonies France imported quantities of valuable timbers in log form and in this form they enjoyed a considerable subsidy from the Government. On arrival, they were cut in French mills and the sawn goods exported to Britain where, because of the subsidy on the logs, they competed quite easily with similar material from British territories. Right up to the collapse the French had been sending cheap softwoods as well which came from the forest areas around Bordeaux, a fact, incidentally, which should have served as a striking example to this country of what can be done with sand, good afforestation laws and an energetic forestry policy. The Landes country was too sandy to be useful agricultural land, but it was turned in the space of a few decades into a forest territory capable of producing useful quantities of usable timber, known by the name of "maritime pine".

Another mysterious name amongst Britain's European suppliers in normal times is Portugal but here too the explanation is simple. All the exports from that country consisted of pit-props, the production of which suited the small but regularly grown trees which are scattered over the lands of England's oldest ally.

The remaining pre-war European exporters of any importance were Czechoslovakia, Rumania and Yugoslavia, although in normal times the natural markets for the last-named countries were the southern European states and the Mediterranean area. Rumania was never of very great importance for this reason, and also because the shipment of her goods was difficult direct from the Black Sea ports. She did, however, send quantities of both hard and softwoods, the former usually coming through Hamburg, Bremen or Danzig, and the latter in most cases direct from Galatz or Constanza. Her timber lands, particularly the hotly disputed territory of Transylvania, comprise some of the most beautiful country in Europe, with treed mountains, green fields, clear streams and rivers running through the verdant valleys. The country of Transylvania is aptly named, and it is unfortunate that the Hungarians and the Rumanians have each done the most ridiculous things—not the least of which was to enter the war on Germany's side—in their dispute over this beautiful land.

The Czechs took the job of timber production far more seriously, and in many branches of activity they had made very great strides. In the eastern provinces, particularly at the foothills of the Carpathian Mountains, they had mills which would compare favourably with any in Europe, and the problems of controlling cutting and re-planting were being met and solved. Their export production was almost entirely hardwoods and their speciality the beech tree which grows in such

SAWN SOFTWOOD IMPORTS INTO U.K. IN 1937

Country	Standards
FINLAND	495,922
U.S.S.R.	444,413
CANADA	366,631
SWEDEN	286,115
POLAND	208,362
LATVIA	75,569
U.S.A.	52,596
JUGO-SLAVIA	34,860
ESTONIA	31,018
other countries	68,216
TOTAL	2,063,702

In addition to the above total, there was an import of about 327,800 stds. of "prepared" softwoods in 1937.

profusion in that part of Europe. In addition to ordinary lumber, they had begun to develop the chemical extraction of a great range of products from wood to a degree which was only reached elsewhere on the Continent by the Germans. Since the main timber areas were in the East, their extension depended upon the provision of adequate transport facilities, and the link-up with the Polish and German railway systems was rapid and efficient. It must be assumed that the splendid forests in the Carpathian and Tatra Mountains will have suffered severely at the hands of the rapacious conquerors. In fact, in all occupied countries of Europe, it will take many years to repair the damage that German overlordship will have wrought, for young trees wantonly felled now are lost for ever to their real owners, and it may take several generations to replace the wealth destroyed in this way. The German use of wood gas and wood alcohol will have led to an immense carnage of European forests, especially the deciduous areas of Czechoslovakia and Yugoslavia. In Czechoslovakia they were also able to take over a number of chemical plants capable of immediate production of a whole range of chemicals and explosives from wood.

For Yugoslavia, the "natural" market was Germany, but exchange difficulties in the pre-war years had led the Yugoslavs to extend their export to this country, in addition to their extensive commerce with the Mediterranean markets. Here, too, the main product was hardwood, and the States of Slovenia and Croatia were the principal areas where beech and ash trees grow in profusion. It is amid some of the best forests of Croatia, Bosnia and Herzegovina that the Partisans are today fighting their most decisive battles with the invaders, and many of these brave men were the foresters and sawyers who worked for a miserable pittance in the sawmills and woods that are scattered in the valleys. In general, Yugoslavia suffers from insufficient railways and roads, particularly in the southern timber producing areas. The main shipping port is Susak and, although this is fairly convenient for the northern parts of the country, further south there is nothing but a narrow gauge railway linking the secondary ports of Split and Dubrovnik to the timber of the hinterland. Around Sarajevo and in Herzegovina province there are a number of sawmills and their natural port is Dubrovnik, which is very small and linked to Sarajevo by a narrow gauge railway, toy-like in appearance, winding its way over the Dinaric Alps—a grand and interesting trip for the lazy wanderer but no cheap highway for bulky timber traffic which has to compete in world markets.

* * * * * *

It was to the forest lands of the New World that Britain was turning more and more in the years that preceded the present war, and in the sister State of Canada she found an efficient and willing supplier. Thousands of square miles of mighty Douglas Fir trees on the Pacific Coast and great areas of smaller but valuable spruce trees in the Eastern

States give Canada paramount importance as a world timber producer. She is also a substantial exporter of a few valuable hardwoods, such as birch and rock elm; an endless list of other timbers of varying commercial value complete her total resources. Firs, hemlocks, cedars, larches, balsam, tamarack, cottonwood, butternut, hickory, poplar, beech, elm and oak appear in stands throughout the country. Some of the native woods have the fresh sounding names that are associated with a country which calls its towns Medicine Hat and Moose Jaw. Among the pines, Limber Pine, Jack Pine, Shore Pine and Lodgepole Pine are unconventional and picturesque, whilst Shagbark Hickory, Chinquapin oak, Sassafras and Staghorn Sumach are hardwoods whose names seem to ring with the rough hardness of the pioneers. These trees do not, of course, grow only in Canada, but many are found over the whole American Continent.

A glance at the map gives the best idea of the enormous area of the Dominion and, although only part of this land mass is populated, vast territories await development and need the men to turn them into rich lands. The total area is just under three and three-quarter million square miles, about one-third of which is covered with trees of all kinds. Not all this treed area contains timber suitable for commercial purposes and a great deal of useful wood is in parts of the country at the moment quite inaccessible. Nearly half-a-million square miles of forests are coniferous, and about 100,000 square miles grow deciduous trees, with a further 220,000 odd square miles with a mixture of both types. A great amount of forest land is classed as "non-productive" and is covered with treed muskeg, treed rock and the sub-alpine and sub-arctic woodlands. There usable timber is not produced since the muskeg is mossy and supports only a mean growth, whilst the sub-alpine and sub-arctic areas are not the most satisfactory for the growing of sizable trees. These unproductive areas are in the far north of the country, and in any event are so distant from modern transport facilities that bringing bulky timber to the world's markets would in normal conditions be impossible. It is in the Eastern States and in British Columbia that the Canadian timber industry has its true homes; in the clear, cold air of east and west pines and spruces grow in profusion.

The largest quantity of standing timber is found in the Eastern Provinces of Ontario, Quebec, New Brunswick and Nova Scotia, where the stands of both hardwood and softwood are very considerable. Next comes British Columbia and the Pacific Coast area where the main stand is softwood with only insignificant quantities of hardwood which are not worth developing commercially. The third producing area is that covered by the Prairie Provinces of Manitoba, Saskatchewan and Alberta growing similar quantities of hard and softwoods with perhaps a little more softwood. Thus Canada is primarily a softwood producing country with a proportion of hardwoods; its main exports are naturally soft timber.

It is said that the first "foreigner" to cut down the trees of British
Columbia was a certain Captain James Cook, who sailed into Nootka
Sound in the year 1778 in search of timber for renewing the masts of
his ship. For some years after that date, many seafarers came upon the
Pacific Coast islands, but none of them ever seems to have realised the
great timber producing possibilities of the area until some fifty years had
passed. Around 1825 David Douglas, botanist, went off to explore the
little known regions of the Pacific Coast in British Columbia, which was
then known as New Caledonia, and gave his name to one of the most
picturesque and useful servants of industry—the Douglas fir tree. It
is a mighty tribute to the unpredictable works of God, rearing straight
and unbending into the rare Columbian air sometimes up to a height of
250 feet. Thousands of trees of Douglas fir are scattered over the face
of a belt of 2,000 miles, running north and south down to the State of
Oregon in the United States and between the Pacific Ocean and the
Rocky Mountains. It is called the Pacific Slope and is one of the largest
timber areas in the world, boasting the giants and the oldest members
of the timber community. Farther south there grows the only rival
to the Douglas fir—the Californian redwood tree—which belongs to
the family of forest monsters. The Northern Central section of the
Pacific Slope is Canada's timber farm, and along the Pacific Coast and
on the watersheds of the Upper Fraser River and the Columbia River
is grown the bulk of her finest lumber.

It is not only in timber wealth that British Columbia is so fortunate;
it almost seems as if man was destined to settle there, and with his axe
fell and saw for the peoples of the world so that others may have houses
built and railways laid. For there all the natural advantages demanded
by a proper timber industry are found. Big trees abound that will pulp
to paper, build houses, bridges, vehicles, aeroplanes—all the numerous
needs of a civilisation at war or peace can be satisfied. To complete the
picture, the rivers and waterways make transport easy, islands line the
miles of rugged coast and provide ideal manufacturing centres from
which the ships of the seven seas may lift their heavy cargoes and carry
them across the oceans. The mild climate means that the harbours are
ice-free all the year round, and operations can go on from one year's
end to the other while there are men to wield an axe and ships to carry
the lumber away. Sawmilling started fairly early in these parts, for
about 1846 the Hudson's Bay Company erected a mill at a small place
called Parsons Bridge.

In the deep forests of the West Coast is to be found most of the
romance which surrounds the lumberman's calling. Thousands of
tough Canadian timber workers spend their days as tree toppers, fellers,
sawyers or labourers in the yards and sawmills.

The job of the tree topper is a particularly dangerous one, and a
lumberman has translated some of this latent danger into his own expres-
sive jargon:—

"Star performers in the year-round drama in which man pits his skill, strength, agility and ingenuity against the forest are the tree toppers or high riggers.

"With a catlike disregard of heights, the tree topper works far above the forest floor, and his job is the necessary prelude to the most spectacular of all Coast logging methods, the high-lead and the sky-line. He strips and tops the spar trees which are the focal point of all such operations. He wears spurs like a telephone lineman's, but longer to penetrate the thick bark of the tree, and a stout belt with a long rope which he passes round the tree and ties through a ring on the other side of the belt. The height at which a tree is topped may vary considerably, but averages from 125 to 130 feet from the ground. When really big trees were more common spars were topped even higher than this, but they are working in smaller timber today and topping is rarely done above 130 feet, the height being dictated by the top diameter, which must not be less than twenty to twenty-two inches. The topping point selected, and the climbing rope adjusted to give him good support but a reasonable amount of play to swing the axe, the topper chops the under cut, side notches it to give a clean break and puts in the back cut, making this about one or two inches higher than the undercut so that the top won't kick back and strike him when it starts to go. With the last stroke, he drops his axe, swings well around to the back of the cut and clings tight to the tree as the top crashes groundward, and the big stick, relieved of the weight of its heavy crown, swings back and forth in a wildly vibrating arc. The force released sometimes causes the spar tip to sway as much as twenty feet to either side of centre.

"With the tree again at rest, the topper's work is done—but not his act, of which a descent by means of a series of quick falls controlled by skilful manipulation of rope and spurs form the hair raising finale, and the goal of every top-notch performer is to toss his canvas headgear into the air and literally 'beat his hat to the ground'. It has been done."

The tree topper's calling has plenty of danger, but the "bucker's" job is just hard work. As soon as the tree has been felled, the bucker follows along behind, marks off the fallen tree trunk and cuts it into lengths suitable for the log mills. The unwritten law of the bucker is that he shall keep close behind the felling crew and "buck" as quickly as they get the trees down on to the ground. Yarders and skidders, gas, steam or Diesel donkeys are employed to bring the logs out of the woods and load them on to the transports. "High-lead" and "sky-line" cable riggers lift the logs and carry them from one part of the wood or clearing to another for loading on to the transports. Most of this equipment can be easily dismantled and set up again where the new felling has been done, although the type of overhead cable transporter known as "steel tower and tree rigged skidders" is more permanent, for some of them employ anything up to ten miles of heavy wire rope.

When the logs, in the lengths as marked by the buckers, have been picked up at the assembly points they are transported to the "booming grounds". These grounds are lake or quiet tidal waters where the logs are shot into the water, sorted into suitable lengths and arranged into booms or rafts. If these rafts have to go down the Pacific Coast, the formation known as the Davis raft is usually used, which is a giant bundle of logs tied firmly together with wire rope so that the whole lot can be safely towed down the shore, or, if the mills are inland, along the river ways to the sawmills for final conversion. The men who man the tow tugs have a big job to do, since down the six or seven hundred miles of coast all kinds of weathers may be encountered and booms sometimes break away during the period of gales. If this happens, thousands of logs may be scattered on the shore to be collected by their owners when the weather clears—and this, as can be imagined, is no simple task! When the logs do arrive at their destination, they are hauled out of the water, selected and graded again and sent to the mill for conversion into the boards, planks and flitches which eventually reach this country.

It is not only in British Columbia that the lumberman's job is full of interest and danger; but the magnitude of the operations there, the extensive forests, the big trees and the numerous mills qualify the Pacific Coast for a leading place in the great timber producing areas of the world. Yet the Eastern States have a higher total potential than the West Coast but the scale of individual operations is in general smaller. The trees are useful but not enormous and the mills are spread throughout the east, the majority of them being small with a correspondingly low output. The main products are pines, spruces and in the hardwood category, birch; it is these timbers that Canada sends in such quantity to the British market. Apart from Britain, the bulk of the remainder of Eastern Canada's output goes to her neighbour, the United States, and in normal years the proportions are something like this—Britain 50-60 per cent. of the total, U.S.A. 25-30 per cent. This is for timber in the solid form, but a considerable amount of the log production of the Eastern States goes into the woodpulp and paper industries which are responsible for so great a part of Canada's export trade. From an economic point of view this area is a more natural source of timber for the British Isles than the Pacific Coast, for the sea haul is so much shorter and more direct than the long journey down the coast and through the Panama which is the route for every piece of Douglas Fir in normal times.

The existence of the third producing area—the Prairie Provinces— may be something of a surprise to those who regard provinces such as Manitoba and Alberta as essentially wheat growing lands where trees are few and far between. In general the area is noted for the number of poplar trees which grow there, but other timbers are available in considerable quantities. In Saskatchewan, for example, good stands of white spruce are found and, although this too is an important wheat growing province, in the early days thousands were employed in the woods in winter and on the land in spring and summer. It was the parkland belt of poplar trees in the northern part of the province that provided the early settlers with timber for fuel and shelter, and was one of the main factors which made the development of the northern wheat belt possible. Today the total productive forest territory in the province is three million acres and its contribution to Canada's total output though limited is important. In Manitoba there are some 250 sawmills, many of which are very small, and a number of pulp and paper mills employing the local raw material.

Such very brief details give some idea of the great potentialities of the Canadian forest lands from the West Coast to the Maritime Provinces in the East. Trade in timber and pulpwood with this country up to the outbreak of the war was increasing, and whatever objections there may be to the principle of import duties and preferences, after the Ottawa Conference Canada by its 10 per cent. preference over such important suppliers as Finland and the Soviet Union was able to capture an ever increasing part of the British market. Before Ottawa, Canada supplied some 6 per cent. of Britain's timber needs against the 19 per cent. of Sweden, 15 of Finland, 12 of the U.S.A. and 10 of Russia. These rough percentages are based upon the value figures for the average of the years 1926-30 and cover all forest products. For the few years prior to the outbreak of war, Canada's share in the total of British imports of timber products had increased to the very remarkable figure of about 17 per cent.; and the Dominion had come to be regarded as one of the most important sources of supply, particularly for constructional softwoods such as Douglas fir and spruce.

The accessible stand of softwood timbers in Canada is sufficient to supply the entire British requirements at the 1938-9 level of consumption for some four hundred years. Although many factors make this statement a little unreal, it serves to illustrate the world importance of Canada's industry. To all this must be added the fact that one of the most important group of exports from Canada is woodpulp and paper products which generally account for a large proportion of her total foreign trade. The trees that grow from the Pacific Coast to the shores of the Atlantic are great wealth, even in the rich lands of the Canadian Dominion; maximum development has by no means been reached, and with the liberation of world trade many will come to share these gifts that nature has bestowed so generously on the North American Continent.

The extensive forest belt which covers British Columbia stretches southwards into the United States and is there equally productive of excellent softwood timber. The general position of United States timber supplies is rather different from that of Canada, since American demand is high, and native wood can be consumed in large quantities so that the export market is not of prime importance, although exports to this country are normally considerable.

The States can be divided roughly into five forest areas, Northern, Central Hardwood, Southern, Rocky Mountain and the Pacific Coast Forests. The last named is not by any means the largest in area, yet it provides the biggest quantity of timber, and is estimated to contain about one-half of the total available standing trees suitable for commercial conversion. Throughout all these forest areas there are mixed belts of soft and hardwoods, although on the Pacific Coast the trees are mainly coniferous. It contains the biggest tree known—the "big tree"—which whilst not of great commercial value has the distinction of attaining a height of up to 330 feet, a diameter of about thirty feet and an age of somewhere in the region of three thousand years. It is a close relation of the Californian Redwood tree already mentioned, but lacks the utility of its taller and thinner brother.

The timber of America is being used up and there are few virgin stands still remaining, although in the valley of the lower Mississippi there are still good quantities of hardwoods. At the present rate of consumption, the States has usable timber to last about fifty years on the assumption that they do nothing by afforestation to replant and prepare for the future. Active steps are now being taken in the States to ensure afforestation. The annual consumption in the United States has been estimated at about twenty-two billion cubic feet and of this total the Pacific Coast is responsible for more than half. The Americans have produced interesting figures to show the relationship between production and consumption of timber per head of the population. During the forty years from 1880 to 1920, population more than doubled, consumption per head of native timber rose until the turn of the century and then fell off, whilst total production went up steadily until about 1906, and then decreased by 1920 to a level not very much above that of 1880. There were manifold reasons for these strange movements, the most obvious of which were the increased importation from foreign countries, the more efficient employment of the timber that was used and the substitution by other materials. No doubt during the period in question total consumption per head of timbers from all sources increased but the development of other sources of supply reduced the relative share of the American grown timber. In normal times, America is both an exporter and importer of timber, since she exports lumber to the British market—mainly hardwoods—and imports quantities of softwoods from the Dominion with whom she has a very satisfactory trading and tariff arrangement. The bulk of her imports are in the form of logs which are cut up in American mills for use in the domestic market. An interesting development which will do something to meet America's demand in the after-war period is the growing exploitation of the timber resources of Alaska, where the opening up of the Alaskan Highway will bring within the range of commercial development a great area abounding with valuable softwood timber. The biggest single item of hardwoods imported by Britain from America was, strangely enough, oak, since the trees of the States produce two kinds of oak very suitable for furniture and a variety of other uses in this country.

There are some other small suppliers, such as Australia and Brazil, but the rest of the picture covers the countries producing in the main hardwood timbers of a very wide variety. Britain drew supplies of hardwoods from about seventy different possessions or foreign countries which ranged from the well-known sources such as Africa and India to wholly unexpected "outsiders"—Iceland, Mexico, Turkey and Ecuador.

From some of these surprise suppliers the quantities exported were very small, and often represented the production of some rare but much desired wood which no other source provided. Another reason may have been a sudden change in the exchange relationship of the two countries which made it temporarily profitable to ship timber to Britain.

* * * * * *

The remaining suppliers of any importance are those who grow and mill two of the most valuable timbers which enter into international exchange—teak and mahogany. There are numerous other woods, particularly from Africa, which were beginning to bulk large in Britain's timber trade, but in total they are much less important than these two. Teak—that is to say genuine teak—is produced in very few countries, and the only important ones in pre-war times were Burma, Siam, the Dutch East Indies and India, and of these the leading producer was Burma, which is the greatest teak growing area in the world. The mahoganies grow in a number of widely spaced areas, the most important of which are some of the Central American States and West Africa, although it is held that the only genuine mahogany is the product of the former area.

Teak enjoys the reputation of being the most romantic and useful of all the timbers which enter into commerce. This romance arises from the method of its production, particularly in the Burmese forests; its usefulness is due to certain inherent qualities possessed by no other kind of timber, hard or softwood. Unlike most woods, teak is very resistant to the effects of changes in atmospheric conditions and to the attacks of fungus; it can therefore be used out of doors without risk of serious deterioration and without the necessity of continual protective painting. It is also acid resistant, and although it will, of course, burn, it is considerably less combustible than the majority of timbers. Some years ago tests were made with eighty-five different timbers and of these only two compared favourably with teak for the slowness of flame penetration. To these very useful features can be added the great strength of the wood, and it is not surprising that teak is in continuous demand for shipbuilding. In the days gone by, the hull of a warship was constructed entirely from teak with a metal sheathing; the fifty years' old cruiser *Warspite* which was recently broken up for salvage contained thousands of teak planks laid end to end to make up its hull. Since this particular vessel was destined, when it was built, to be used on the China station, there was a good reason for this timber because the lower heat conductivity of the wood made it easier to live comfortably below decks in tropical seas. It is for the same reason that today warships and freighters are, wherever possible, decked in teak if they have to spend the majority of their lives in tropical climates; the burning sunshine upon a steel deck creates a hell for those who are forced to live and work below decks.

The romantic side of teak is provided by the unusual methods of production that are employed from the time that the tree is selected for felling until it emerges as a piece of timber ready for consumption. As the bulk of the teak used in this country comes from Burma, it is perhaps unnecessary to deal with any of the other smaller producing areas. As a British possession, Burma's export to this country enjoys a preference over the exports from Siam, Java or any of the other Dutch East Indies. The teak producing forests of Burma cover the relatively small area of 120,000 square miles, and it has been necessary from an early date to operate strict forestry conservation laws to protect supplies. As it is, suitable trees are mixed up in forests containing a whole variety of other species of timber and the normal yield of trees ready for felling every year is no greater than one for every eight to nine acres of forest land. In 1856 a Dr. Brandis was appointed Conservator of Forests, and he proceeded to lay down a conservation programme which was the basis of all the subsequent programmes not only in Burma but also in other producing areas. Up to the outbreak of the war, the production of teak was one of the most important of Burmese industries, employing something like fifty thousand men and bringing to the country's coffers a very large sum in royalties—a fact which made the proper organisation of the forests of prime importance to the people and Government of the country.

Elephants and teak trees have long been associated in the minds of many, and it is to the elephant as much as to the native of Burma that the rest of the world owes a debt as the joint producer of this valuable and beautiful wood. It is the elephant which is largely responsible for solving the greatest problem of teak production—the extraction of huge logs in country which is some of the most difficult in the world. All attempts to introduce mechanical transportation systems have been beaten by two facts. First of all, the quantity of logs available in any one area is very small, so that for most of the time tractors, monkey winches or cable railways would be idle or, what is more serious, they would never be in the right situation for the two season's working. In the case of fixed transport systems, these must be removed to the next available stand which may be many hundreds of miles away. The second reason why modern transport methods are not suitable is the type of country in which these teak forests are found. Many of the areas are impassable except for stony tracks, and even these may be unusable during the rainy season. Apart from the construction of big roadways, which the teak traffic does not justify economically, there is no road system in being which would cover the main teak areas and aid the transport of the logs.

For these reasons, the rivers and the elephants are the main means of extraction, and they have governed to some degree the methods of production employed in Burma. A teak tree takes some one hundred and twenty to one hundred and fifty years to reach full maturity, and when such a mature tree has been chosen for felling it is "girdled". This merely means cutting a ring through the bark to a depth sufficient to expose the heartwood as near the ground as possible in order to stop the flow of sap up the tree: the process of growth then ceases. After about two years, the tree is ready for felling, as during that period it has lost much of its moisture through the girdling process, and when the felled trunk is dragged to the rivers it will float. The density of teak is such that this is the only method which will ensure that the trunks float on the rivers, for if they did not float, the costs of transport would be quite prohibitive, and teak would only be used in very small quantities for special work instead of being one of the most valuable commercial woods. It is in the job of dragging the mighty logs through woods and jungle, over every kind of obstacle to the banks of streams that the elephant has proved such a cheap and efficient means of transport. Some five thousand elephants as well as ten thousand buffaloes are used for this work. The elephant is the more satisfactory beast of burden, not only because of its greater strength and intelligence, but also because it can find all the food it needs in the forests where the teak trees grow; the internal combustion engine requires tons of food to keep it going, the elephant feeds as it goes along. These kindly looking giants with their self-sufficiency and their flair for team work provide an efficient means of transport that many generations of mechanical progress have not yet rendered obsolete.

Once in the larger rivers, the logs are strung together into rafts to be sent down to the ports or clearing centres for conversion at the mills there. These rafts are usually in charge of rafters who build their makeshift shacks upon the rafts and travel downstream, accompanied by their families and hosts of domestic pets. There are many excitements and not a few dangers for these strange water gypsies, for logs break loose or rafts become stranded on low banks, and sometimes the situation is such that only the help of a friendly elephant will save the rafts from destruction. The elephant does not just push and pull until something happens to set the raft free again, but with an uncanny insight will carefully select the log which is the cause of all the trouble and, standing deep in the rushing torrents, will heave the offender out until the rafts or logs are free once more to continue their journey downstream. In the monsoon period work of this kind can be very dangerous, and the elephant riders take risks for their few shillings pay which would seem fantastic to any western worker. With a good elephant, however, the man on top has very little to fear.

This is the romantic side of teak, and the efforts of these simple natives and their lumbering elephants do bring to the shipbuilders and industrialists of the Western world a timber which has been of great service to man. Only about a quarter of the production of Burma comes to Europe, the main part of the balance is exported to India where teak is also grown but not on so large a scale.

The other hardwood which rivals teak in importance is mahogany and, although this wood is not so valuable, it is nevertheless exported in very large quantities from the Central American States and West Africa. It can be employed for many purposes, and before the war was one of the most widely used of the more expensive types of hardwoods not only where ease of working and strength were required, but also for its very fine decorative qualities. Mahogany has been known for more than two hundred years, and appears to have originated in the West Indies, where it was exploited by the Spaniards for ship construction work as long ago as the middle of the sixteenth century. Raleigh is said to have used the wood for ship repair work, and presented Queen Elizabeth with a piece of furniture made from the wood after one of his visits to the Indies. It was not until the eighteenth century that it became a regularly imported material and began to be used for furniture and cabinet making to adorn the elegant work of Chippendale, Adam, Heppelwhite and, later on, Sheraton. Ever since those distant days, it has been imported in increasing quantities for ship and boat building, furniture, patterns, fine joinery and many other uses where taste and the ability to pay were the governing factors. In recent years many strange timbers have acquired the name of "mahogany", which, in fact, are not of the mahogany family at all, and it is these cheaper kinds which found a use in mass-produced furniture, treated and polished to look remarkably like the real thing, but lacking the colour and fineness of grain of genuine mahogany.

British Honduras has for long been the home of some of the finest types of mahogany, but the most convenient outlet for the production of this Colony is obviously the United States, and it is to the States that the majority of the timber goes in peace time. Recently the main problem has been the old one of the development of transport facilities since the ordinary means of timber transport—waterways—are quite satisfactory when the raw material is near to the rivers, but as the area worked extends the felling is done farther and farther away from the rivers and other means are necessary to get the logs to the waterways. In Honduras, too, some of these rivers are very small, and the rainy season is irregular so that the logs may be stranded for a whole year with insufficient rain to fill the river beds and float off the logs. The use of American tractors and similar devices should meet the need; but it is an expensive method in comparison with present native labour, and this problem has tended to limit to a certain extent the output from the Colony. With the early solution of these difficulties, the future is promising for the Honduras timber industry.

The other main mahogany producing area outside the Central American States is the West Coast of Africa from which great quantities of mahogany logs have reached Britain since the turn of the century. The trade with British West Africa started about one hundred years ago, but it was not until the eighteen eighties that the import began to reach considerable proportions, and ever since it has developed apace. The logs were usually known by the ports or districts from which they came: there was Benin, Lagos, Sekondi and Grand Bassam mahogany (the last-named a product of French territory), and a whole series of other kinds identified by the port of shipment and bought and sold on the reputation of the type or quality of mahogany which was normally shipped from that particular port or milled in that area. In the main all this export was in the form of solid logs which were floated down the rivers during the rainy season and shipped from the coastal areas to this country. Unlike the Burmese trade in teak which had its extensive mills for conversion at ports such as Rangoon and Moulmein, the West African ports were not the scenes of sawmilling activities until quite recently, when a number of mills have been erected, particularly in the French territories. The logs were shipped in tree trunk form and were usually sold in the public auctions in the ports of arrival, particularly in London and Liverpool. It was a special trade calling for highly skilled inspectors who could estimate the kind of wood that a log would yield, and enormous prices have been called in the Liverpool mahogany auction sales. In one case some years ago three logs all cut from the same tree fetched the record price of £3,130, probably because they were of the type of wood rated very highly for certain kinds of furniture production.

Nigeria is particularly prolific in excellent types of mahogany, and the forestry services there have been brought to a high pitch of efficiency. The same difficulty which faces both Burma and Honduras exists in Nigeria—the stands of timber nearest to the rivers and waterways are becoming exhausted and each new season's felling has to take place farther afield which at once forces the authorities to meet the transport problem. There are many who believe, too, that an essential part of the foundation of a really permanent timber producing industry in this part of Africa must be action by the Government to see that the lion's share of the country's wealth is re-invested in the education and improvement of the social conditions of the natives who actually work the lumber. There is great scope for wise colonial statesmanship in these areas, for here Britain could bring to the backward peoples of equatorial Africa a fair system of government with a major stake in the economic development of the lands where they have lived for centuries.

There remain but few important suppliers of timber to this country in peace time not covered by what has already been said. From strange, unlikely places are drawn very useful quantities of timber, as for example the import of a wood known as "lauan" from the Philippines. It is a cheap timber and takes the place of mahogany in low priced productions; in fact, it is sometimes referred to as Philippine mahogany—a misleading name since it is not of the mahogany family at all. From Borneo comes another timber which in recent years has found many uses in the shipbuilding industry and has partly replaced teak as a material for ship's decks. It is called "serayah", and it too is sometimes incorrectly referred to as "Borneo mahogany". These are not the farthest distances from which the timber used by industry in Britain can come. Japan was an important supplier of oak and ash and was beginning to develop the resources of stolen Manchuria at the outbreak of war. It seems strange but from the tiny overcrowded islands of Japan, across thousands of miles of sea, came oak for the traders of Britain, where for centuries oak has been the commonest tree to be seen from the Tweed to the Trent, from the Trent to the Severn.

Australia has nearly fifty thousand square miles of land capable of producing usable timber, and from these forests Britain has for many years drawn a few special woods which were long ago found suitable for particular jobs. Two woods with the almost music hall names of "jarrah" and "karri" grow in Western Australia, and are sent to this country in considerable quantities for shipyard work, bridge building, pavings and similar construction purposes, whilst the turpentine tree is employed in harbour building and underwater work. Naturally, because of the distance of the country from the main world markets and the demands of industry at home, the trade in wood from Australia was never on a great scale, and it was seldom more than a very small percentage of the total exported from one of the more important producing countries such as the United States.

The balance of the peacetime providers of Britain's vast timber imports are spread irregularly over the face of the earth, but each individual country is responsible only for a minute proportion of the whole. Several of the South American States, such as Brazil, Peru, Venezuela, Paraguay and Ecuador were exporters in a small way, whilst many relatively unimportant territories from Nicaragua to Madagascar produced exportable lumber. They are either too numerous or too sporadic to merit mention amongst the timber aristocrats who make up the list of producers of Britain's forty to sixty million pounds worth of timber imports each year.

The way this great total value of imports is divided up amongst the various suppliers can be illustrated by taking the figures of a pre-war year. The list below gives the values of imports from the countries shown to the United Kingdom for all kinds of wood and timber for the year 1937. The imports of plywood and other types of semi-manufactured and manufactured timber materials are not included:—

	1937 £
British West Africa	344,643
British India	1,154,811
Australia	313,381
Canada	9,223,876
Other British Countries	921,633
Soviet Union	10,100,898
Finland	11,078,323
Estonia	674,303
Latvia	2,871,542

VALUES OF IMPORTS INTO U.K. IN 1937

Br. West Africa	£	344,643
Japan	£	668,359
Estonia	£	674,303
Norway	££	772,567
France	££	1,145,623
Br. India	££	1,154,811
Jugoslavia	££	1,229,038
Other Br. Countries	££	1,235,014
Other Fgn. Countries	£££££	2,710,314
Latvia	£££££	2,871,542
Poland	£££££££££	5,190,500
U.S.A.	£££££££££	5,367,816
Sweden	££££££££££££££	8,056,246
Canada	££££££££££££££££	9,223,876
U.S.S.R.	£££££££££££££££££	10,100,898
Finland	£££££££££££££££££££	11,078,323

TOTAL £61,823,873

The figures given comprise softwood and hardwood imports, but do
not include plywood, veneers or manufactured wood-goods.

Sweden ...	...	...	...	...	...	8,056,246
Norway ...	...	...	...	...	...	772,567
Poland ...	...	...	...	...	...	5,190,500
Germany	...	...	...	...	...	101,382
France ...	...	...	...	...	...	1,145,623
Portugal	...	...	...	...	...	304,779
Jugoslavia	...	...	...	...	...	1,229,038
Japan ...	...	...	...	...	...	668,359
United States of America	...	...	...	...	5,367,816
Philippine Islands	...	...	...	...	...	128,537
Other Foreign Countries	...	...	...	...	2,175,616
Total ...	...	...	...	...	...	61,823,873

*   *   *   *   *   *

There is still one peace-time timber supplier that has not been mentioned—Britain herself; and since later on the place that Britain is occupying in the job of war-time timber supply will be examined, little need be said here of her position as a timber-producing country prior to this war. About 5 to 7½ per cent. of the quantity consumed was home produced; in value terms the percentage was about 3½. Apart from pit-props, which were used in considerable quantities from home-grown material, the bulk of the production was in the lower grades for agricultural purposes or for domestic use where cheapness was important and the quality did not so much matter. In spite of this very small consumption, Britain was in fact using up more of her timber resources than was annually accruing to her by the growing up of trees. In other words, Britain's native timber consumption, though so small in comparison with her needs, was nevertheless greater than her annual increment. Mills there were dotted more or less indiscriminately over the countryside as a whole, but many of them were only working on short time, others were idle altogether, and the production of most of them was of the lowest grade of timber to meet the needs of those who wanted fences, gates and similar rough articles.

There were some firms in the native timber production that had managed to survive generations of trading, but they were few, and their existence was entirely due to their efforts in developing those useful and well demanded specialities such as home-grown ash and very good quality oak, and in bringing to their calling rare qualities of foresight and skill which enabled them to make a livelihood from an industry in the strongest competition with other producing countries, competitors who had the advantage of plentiful supplies, and, in most cases, virgin stands of timber upon which to work. In general, however, production and marketing were based upon arrangements so haphazard that it is miraculous any firms contrived to keep their heads above water, particularly in the difficult depression years in the early 'thirties. Although there were a few progressive individuals connected with the industry, the attitude was normally defeatist, and little effort was spent in trying to develop that share of the total British timber consumption which could have been guided towards home-felled material. The whole situation was not easy, and more must be said on the matter in a later chapter dealing with the Forestry Reports and the future of forestry in this country. There were attempts to obtain a duty on imported timber in 1932, but the Import Duties Advisory Committee decided that there was insufficient evidence to show the existence of an efficient industry capable of providing the required timber at reasonable prices if foreign imports were restricted. It is quite obvious that to have acceded to the request of the home producers in 1932 would have led to a disastrous increase in prices and a complete failure to provide the supplies demanded by industry. The war of 1914-18 had resulted in the dissipation of so much of the available raw material that the industry never really got on its feet again, and year by year lack of markets and organisation weakened what had once been a flourishing trade.

"I again affirm, that had these advantages of forest
culture been then vigorously encouraged and promoted,
there had now been of those materials infinite store, even
from the very acorn and seminary, a competent advance
of the most useful timber for the building of ships (as I
think is sufficiently made out) since his late Majesty's
Restoration: The want of timber and the necessity of
being supply'd by foreign countries, if not prevented by
better and more industrious instruments, may prove in a
short time a greater mischief to the publick, than the late
diminution of the coin. I wish I prove no prophet, whilst
I cannot for my life but often think of what the learned
Melanchthon above a hundred years since was wont to
say (long before those barbarous wars had made these
devastations in Germany), that the time was coming,
when the want of three things would be the ruin of
Europe, *lignum, probam monetam, probos amicos*; timber,
good money, and sincere friends. How far we see this
prediction already verify'd, let others judge."

JOHN EVELYN: *Sylva*

CHAPTER II

SUPPLIES FOR WAR

THE OUTBREAK of the war in Europe at once changed the entire
supply position for Britain, and sources from which a great quantity
of useful timbers was expected were overnight placed within the range
of the enemy. But even before the war actually began in Poland, the
political events of Europe had gravely endangered the British timber
supply. The first victim was the State which became a slave territory
at Munich—Czechoslovakia. The total export from this Central European
country was never very large, but it played a part in the provision of
certain kinds of cheap timber and, although in theory Czechoslovakia
was still free to export after Munich, everyone but Lord Runciman
knew that her freedom to trade had passed away with her political
freedom. A few firms evacuated their offices from Prague to Budapest
or to some town in Northern Yugoslavia in the hope of being able to
carry on in relative peace; but it was very soon evident that the Germans
wanted timber from the Czechs along with arms and munitions far more
than they cared about the "emancipation" of the miserable Sudeten
Germans. Apart from the few tons of timber which some far-sighted
millers had loaded into railway wagons and sent rolling to Danzig or
Hamburg, the supply from Czechoslovakia ceased abruptly with the
German occupation.

The loss of the Czechoslovakian output was largely a hardwood loss and therefore could be replaced from many other sources in Europe; but the invasion of Poland was the end of a softwood supplier at a time when the demand for softwoods for war work was just beginning. Once again the Allies or Allies-to-be suffered a diminution in supplies which some would have thought sufficient to affect visibly their war effort. For two reasons this was not so. First, in the early days of the war the tempo of activity was so slow that the loss of a few suppliers of raw material made very little difference; and secondly, this country had fair stocks and could therefore live for some time at least. The production of Poland was a useful one, not only because of the excellent quantity of softwoods received, but also because of the hardwoods and plywoods which had been arriving in increasing amount during the five years which preceded the war.

During the attack on Poland, a few ships continued to come through the Baltic from the other producing countries, including the Soviet Union, but the rapid development of the war was soon to deprive the United Kingdom of the bulk of its softwood shipments almost at one stroke. In the last few weeks of 1939, the Russian-Finnish war temporarily ended shipment from the Soviet Union and made it impossible for the Finns to send the usual proportion of their annual output of softwoods. Thus by the beginning of 1940, Britain had lost practically the whole of her European supply of softwood timbers—all, that is to say, with the exception of occasional lots carried by the ships that could get through from Norway and Sweden. What this really meant in cold fact can be seen from the figures. In 1938, for example, Britain imported from Poland, Czechoslovakia, Russia, Finland and the Baltic countries of Latvia, Lithuania and Estonia some million standards of softwoods out of a total import of just under two million standards. So that more than half the normal exports to Britain had been cut by 1940.

This was serious enough, but even greater blows were to be dealt by the middle of the crisis year. Norway and Sweden ceased to be suppliers, Norway because she was occupied by the enemy and Sweden since it was virtually impossible to ship materials from the country with the Germans in possession of Norway and Denmark. A few ships did get through, but so few that they could not be regarded as a serious contribution to the needs of the United Kingdom. This second stroke of bad fortune meant the loss of a further potential annual import of about four hundred thousand standards, so that some two-thirds of Britain's normal supply was now either controlled by the enemy or could only be shipped through waters dominated by his nearby submarine, surface craft and airplane bases. The European suppliers were reduced to Yugoslavia, Rumania and small quantities from France and Belgium. From Yugoslavia certain imports were arranged, but these were mostly in hardwood, and the shipping difficulty was so great that only a little actually arrived; a similar position existed with Rumania where the haul was much longer and necessitated bringing ships right the way through the Mediterranean. The quantities from Belgium and France were very small and soon these too were cut off entirely, although the potential in France was fairly considerable, as the last war had shown that the forests of Gascony alone could be expected to yield a good amount of lower grade softwood timbers. The other producing areas in France were too near the Maginot Line to be of any value after the declaration of war, and in any event the wild mobilisation which dragged all conscripts from their work and rushed them to arms was so drastic that most of the sawmills were left without sufficient labour to meet even the needs of French industry.

The capitulation of France and the entry of Italy into the war finally solved the problem of European timber supplies, for henceforth there was none available to the British nation. Yugoslavia still stood but no shipping could be spared, and if there was a ship free here and there no escorts were available to see them through the now dangerous waters of Mussolini's *mare nostrum*. The position was very different from the last war, when the Scandinavian countries were able to supply many needs and France still stood to use her resources to meet a few of the requirements of the front in the West. During 1914-18 the neutrality of Norway and Sweden enabled shipments to reach the Allies and in the early days of that war, Russia was also able to send a proportion of her immense production to Britain. In this war, the main weight of the responsibility of supplying Britain fell eventually upon Canada and the United States during a period when the U-boat menace was as great as at any time in the last war. This change in the origin of supplies has meant a greater drain upon available shipping space, for whereas in the Great War these bulky cargoes had only to be brought from the Baltic countries, since 1940 practically all the ships carrying timber have had to face the hazardous Atlantic crossing, so that something like twice as much shipping is needed to carry the same tonnage of timber in any year.

What is actually happening to the Continental producers today cannot be ascertained, but the little pieces of information which do leak out inevitably tell the same sad story. Throughout Europe the trees are being cut down regardless of afforestation rules, the age of the trees or the value of the timber. The crisis in the Nazis transport arrangements prevents the despatch of coal to all the areas that need it, and wood is used as fuel in many parts of occupied territory. Reports coming out of Norway speak of the heavy cutting of trees there and an annual felling far in excess of the yearly increment; if the owners will not carry out the orders of the Germans, then hordes of Russian prisoners are brought in who are quickly forced to do the job. One of the most valuable forest areas in Norway, near Eidsvoll, was treated in this manner. In all occupied countries the Germans naturally have a very big demand for timber huts and dwellings to house their numerous troops and police forces, and in the eagerness to get the huts built they care neither for the future of the area as a producer nor for the feelings of the local inhabitants and the axe falls. It is, of course, unreasonable to expect the would-be conquerors to be squeamish about destroying trees when they show few signs of conscience at the hanging and shooting of a thousand or more Russians.

The loss of the European suppliers was not, however, the end of the grim story, for a year later the entry of Japan into the war against Britain and the United States cut off from the West the valuable timber areas of Burma and the East Indies, from which large quantities of teak and other useful hardwoods were arriving to play their part in the struggle. The small imports from Australia and New Zealand which for some purposes were important, also stopped through lack of escorts on a long and perilous journey, and the hardwoods of the North American Continent had to be called in to fill the gaps left by the loss of Burma, Siam, Java and numerous small producers throughout the Pacific and Indian Oceans. Not only did these latest developments mean a reduction in the number of areas from which useful timber could be drawn, but what was even more damaging at that time, the extension of the submarine and aircraft war from the Atlantic to the Pacific, to the Indian Ocean—in fact to every ocean where Allied ships were accustomed to sail—entailed new and heavy demands on Navies already overburdened with the tasks in hand. Many people failed to appreciate the very serious plight in which Britain found herself, and few have heard the story of how it was possible to overcome these difficulties and lay the sure foundations of the offensives which have already unfolded and the others which are about to begin. So far as timber supplies were concerned, the steps taken to meet the crisis which followed Dunkirk and became accentuated by Pearl Harbour can be divided into two.

There was first of all the expansion of output in the North American Continent, particularly Canada, which provided Britain with an ever increasing quantity of both hard and softwoods. Those hardwoods which could not be obtained from the temperate zones in North America were provided by the tropical forest lands of Africa, from which area increasing quantities of valuable hardwoods were shipped as tonnage became available. The second step was the frantic speeding-up of the production of timber from native trees of the British Isles, a development which was very slow to start but which eventually exceeded the most optimistic estimates of the experts, and has done something really solid in assuring sufficient supplies of timber for a nation fighting for its life on three continents. The war-time rôle played by home production is important enough to be dealt with in some detail, since without this great expansion a major part of the war effort would have been impossible of achievement.

*   *   *   *   *   *

The contribution of the Canadians to the British war effort generally is well known though perhaps not in any detail. What was principally an extensive, agricultural land blossomed rapidly into an industrial producer of the first rank, and has given to the united Allied cause not only brave soldiers, sailors and airmen, but a whole host of industrial products from raw materials to the finished aeroplanes, tanks, trucks, guns and ammunition. Among the agricultural products food and timber were two of the most important, both being natural exports from Canada even in peace time.

The total softwood export of Canada has increased since the years before the last war by some 30 per cent., and the share of this total taken by the mother country has gone up from one-third to well over one-half of the exportable quantity. The other important buyer of Canada's softwoods has been her near neighbour, the U.S.A., whose share was nearly equal to that of Britain in a number of pre-war years. Despite these very considerable export figures, Canada before this war began had a number of mills, particularly on the West Coast, which were idle, and this sleeping potential was rapidly brought into operation to meet the urgent demands of Britain. After years of difficult trading, many mills had been forced to shut down or to reduce their operations considerably; today they are roaring away cutting the huge Douglas fir trees into the lumber urgently needed by the Allied countries in their war effort. The main factor was not the quantity that could be wrested from the woods and mills; it was how much shipping space could be allowed for the long haul from the Pacific Coast to the west of England, some nine thousand miles, for timber is a very bulky cargo and such a journey ties up shipping for many months. Not only are the cargoes bulky, but much of this "bulk" so carefully convoyed across a U-boat studded Atlantic is eventually dissipated in the waste which is inevitable in converting ordinary timber to the sizes industry requires. Iron, steel and other metals can be manufactured and any waste re-melted down to be utilised afresh; but sawdust and ends of timber cleaned off in the process of conversion have very little use other than for stoking the boilers. There was no industry in this country ready to change wood waste and sawdust to chemicals, explosives or other valuable derivatives, and to have founded such an industry at a time when the prime need was for more guns, aeroplanes and tanks would have retarded the growth of the desperately needed forces. There was no fund of skilled labour available for chemical production from wood or for distillation plants, and without doubt Britain has lost a chance in peace time to build up an industry which would have been of inestimable value to her in the war that seemed a certainty ever since the early 'thirties.

The problem of freighting timber these vast distances from Canada led to the attempt to rail cargoes across the 2,000 miles of Canada from west to east and ship them from the east coast where facilities were not so good, but at least the sea voyage was only some 3,000 miles, and large quantities of shipping would not be tied up for weeks on end in the voyage around Panama. This helped a little, although it was not possible to handle very great tonnages by this means; when, however, the Americans entered the war and production in the U.S.A. was greatly stepped up, the North American Continent needed every rail car it could get to keep the great armament factories served, and the railways could not be spared for the transport of timber from the Pacific Coast to American ports or to the St. Lawrence. The entry of America into the war also had other consequences in Canada which caused repercussions over here. The United States began to increase their demand for just the same Canadian timber as the war effort in Britain so badly needed; naturally, a system of priorities was instituted, but it was not always possible to operate it with due consideration to the British so many miles away across the Atlantic Ocean. The development of American industry geared up to war production has been so phenomenal that the slack of Canadian production has been readily absorbed without meeting all the requirements. The real shortage was not felt until this country had the ships it needed to carry a reasonable supply—and then the full effects of American demand began to be obvious. Before shipping was the scarce commodity and the Canadians could provide all the timber that there were ships to carry; today there are ships to carry very large quantities, but the timber is wanted on the American Continent itself. The efforts that the Canadians are making to produce what is required are superb; to some extent they are succeeding, but certain woods which are scarce have been the cause of considerable difficulties between the Americans and the British purchasing commissions.

The Americans themselves have increased their production and are now exporting notable quantities, mostly hardwoods, to the U.K. under the terms of the Lend-Lease arrangements. Here, too, there are difficulties, since it is becoming practically impossible to spare timbers which are so badly needed for America's own war effort, still extending month by month. Yet the United States have delivered shipments of oak, ash and similar hardwood timbers which have been invaluable to Britain in meeting the many demands which her earlier maturing war effort made on timber supplies.

Available shipping has been the main factor limiting the supplies that reach Britain from the few remaining producers. These are the Central American States, Brazil and the various territories of the Continent of Africa. From Africa in particular the export has been extended, and the forests of the West Coast both British and French have supplied vast quantities of mahogany and other valuable woods to meet the heavy demands of the ship and boat builders and a variety of other war users. Timbers whose names were unfamiliar to many in this country began to arrive to replace those lost through enemy advances. The three best known woods imported from this area before the war were mahogany, obeche and iroko, the last-named timber enjoying many of the virtues and something of the appearance of teak so that it earned the botanically erroneous name of "African teak". The situation demanded replacements, and to this list were added a hundred or so other giants from the tropical forests of West Africa—ekki, idigbo, dahoma, opepe and a whole host more with equally unusual names. The Belgian Congo lands also yield timber in profusion, a great deal of which is suitable for conversion for war purposes. In peace time, the greater part of the export of logs from the Congo went direct to Antwerp where, in the French manner, these logs were sawn up and either exported in lumber form or disposed of in the local Belgian markets. Even to this country in those days came woods with the pleasantly ringing names of limbawood and kambala; in war time the Belgian Colonial Empire has been freely giving its economic resources and raw materials to the Allies.

The French resources in West Africa are much more valuable and of greater extent. Large stands of mahoganies and similar woods and a milling organisation which is better than that normally found on the coast of Africa existed not only in French Equatorial Africa but also in the great area of French West Africa. The main part of both these territories joined the Fighting French at an early stage and brought over considerable supplies of mahogany and gaboon, woods which are now serving in many of the Allies' fighting ships, to select but one of the many uses to which the timbers have been put. Now the employment of these vast timber yields of the West Coast of Africa is limited only by the amount of shipping space that can reasonably be allocated to their shipment. It is certain that after the war, on these bleak, unhealthy coasts there will have been created an industry which will be in a position to capture many of the markets of the world which its lack of equipment and knowledge prevented it from acquiring before 1939.

The remaining war-time suppliers to Britain's war effort were very few, but the development of several timbers indigenous to Brazil is worth mentioning. Brazil has great treed areas but little is known at present about most of the timbers, and the transport facilities of this huge country are so undeveloped that there are numerous difficulties to be overcome before timber can be shipped. The shipments sent have been very useful and, in the case of one kind of timber called Parana pine, its use has been extended to aircraft construction with some success. Other woods are the subject of experiments to test their values in comparison with the timbers which the war has put outside the range of the British user, and it is certain that valuable substitutes will be discovered whose usefulness should not pass away entirely with the arrival of peace.

This catalogue of disasters to Britain's timber supply was on a par with the general losses that the country suffered after Dunkirk in every part of the world, and the position naturally became more and more difficult. It is true that many of these troubles could hardly have been foreseen in the years before the war when planning for the feared eventuality was in progress, and it is not easy with the information at present available to say whether those responsible for the plans in the event of any future war should have had sufficient foresight to assess the broad outline of possible losses of sources of supply and to make preparations accordingly. However, when the blow at last fell, those in control realised the necessity for an immediate expansion in the output from the English and Scottish forest lands, and although their early measures were far too timid in the face of such a menacing situation, they did try to produce the necessary timber and in the end, with the help of the industry itself, the output rose rapidly. Timber had to be found somewhere, and once more the trees of the English countryside came to the rescue of a nation fighting for its very existence and facing early defeat. Just as the oaks had made the men-o'-war which saved England from invasion in the days gone by, so the oaks and beeches, pines and larches have this time come to the aid of the country in its preparations to repel yet another Continental invader.

The simple-minded man can be pardoned for asking why this crisis ever arose in view of the history of past wars and the complete dependence of Britain on imported timber in times of peace. Had there been no one with the foresight to plan so that just such a crisis could be avoided? Apart from the actions of the Forestry Commission since its inception in 1919, very little had been done by any Government to conserve supplies or to see that there was sufficient timber in the country at any one moment to meet emergencies. Such a step would be practicable, since timber if properly treated will last in store for an indefinite period; in many cases it actually improves with keeping like a good brandy. No; those in charge had to start right from scratch in their attempt to make up from home production all that had been lost in the first year of war.

The result of these losses was to leave no possible alternative to the felling of as many trees in the woods of the United Kingdom as were suitable for timber conversion. No one really knew exactly how much such timber there was since there had never been a proper survey of tree wealth; it was just a question of getting busy with axe and saw and felling the most accessible areas first. There was, of course, no machinery to control felling, no powers to compel owners of suitable trees to fell, no means of assuring that the best trunks were converted to the most useful lumber. All the controls, which now exist, were imposed clause by clause as the requirements of the situation demanded it from day to day.

When the full effect of the proposals to cut down so much of the woodlands of England and Scotland was realised, many voices were raised to protest against the damage that was to be done to the beautiful countryside of Britain, and it is as well to meet this point at once. The argument lacks any sense of proportion at a time when everything was being thrown into the scales against Nazism and Fascism. Young men give their lives; other strange people complain about a few trees that are lost to their view. It is the flight from reason of the unthinking. Let them consider what happens in countries overrun by the enemy forces —there the wanton, useless destruction of modern war eats up every living thing, man and trees. There the soil is poisoned with blood and the trees blasted up by the roots; the countryside that the Russians knew and loved is a mass of twisted metal, shattered trees and derelict dwellings. Here a few stately trees fall to the woodman's axe to be converted to the instruments of war so that proud, free people may remain proud and free. Here trees go to make ships to bring arms and food to the oppressed peoples, to carry armies to their deliverance and succour to their women and children.

There will be many blank spaces where once a tree has stood; for each one will have gone to play its part in the fight for freedom. In the more enlightened days of the future when afforestation is part of the policy of the country, those who resist the scientific felling of trees will cry crocodile tears, for trees should be regarded as a crop, and who would weep because in good time some yellow wheat field has to be reaped that man may eat? How much longer is it possible to enjoy the pleasures of the trees of the countryside than the corn in the fields, for the one will be there for the span of a man's life, the other for a short summer only. Let those who oppose the bringing of the forests into the service of man's economic life reflect upon the reasons that lie behind their apparent concern for the beauties of the hills and dales of Britain. Many resist because the traditions of the past have given them the right to enjoy and survey their woods and forests in solitude; or their desire to shoot or hunt in seclusion. But the sole enjoyment of vast tracks of the countryside is not an inalienable right of any citizen of twentieth century Britain, much less can such persons claim to say what is good or bad for a Britain fighting for her existence against the Fascist hordes. Those who, in peace time, shared the beauties of their surroundings with others have earned the ear of their countrymen; but others who shut themselves behind high walls like feudal lords and nailed on to trees warnings that trespassers would be prosecuted cannot now expect their piteous defence of rural England to be treated seriously.

In peace time, under 10 per cent. of the quantity of timber consumed in this country was supplied from the home mills and, although during war time the total consumption is greatly reduced by the prohibition of the use of timber for anything but priority purposes, it can be readily seen that to meet the whole demand is nigh on an impossibility. Again, the fact that so small a proportion of peace-time consumption was produced at home meant that in general the mills were both unprofitable and small. There were very few that possessed up-to-date machinery capable of producing a reasonable output of sawn material, for the type of trade to which they had become accustomed during the years when imports were flowing freely into Britain did not equip them to meet the new and very different demands of war and, although they struggled bravely to play their part in the new conditions, it soon became obvious that radical changes were needed to increase production. The rapid increase in production occasioned some very ticklish problems, since labour was becoming scarce because of the heavy calls for armies and industry; and transport facilities—again of vital importance with so bulky an article—began to be more difficult to provide.

The problem of providing the necessary labour applied not only to work in the sawmills but also to the felling and preparation of the logs for conversion. There had always been a certain small labour force for felling and cleaning in the woods, work which, although it seems to be easy, nevertheless calls for a high degree of skill. New men were recruited as fellers but the main supply came from the forestry companies provided by Dominion and Colonial army units. The Canadians had been well known in many woodland areas in the last war, and once again they came to the rescue with their up-to-date methods to work the forests of Scotland, where the majority of them were stationed. These men are soldiers as well as timbermen, and undergo rigorous training in ordinary military duties so that they can be used for operational tasks at any time they are needed. In addition, there were contingents from New Zealand, Newfoundland and Australia; and a few companies of British forest workers, organised in units of the Royal Engineers. These soldiers filled gaps and did valuable work for which it would have been impossible to spare trained men from the labour force available in this country. To some of them, accustomed to the immense spaces of Australia or Canada and the gargantuan trees that grow there, the trunks of the Scottish forests must have seemed like a small job; but their arrival was timely, for it would have been impossible to provide all the logs that the mills needed with the labour force then available.

There is much to be done before the log is finally sawn. Logs must be measured, graded and marked so that the miller knows what they are and to what sizes they should be converted when he gets them into his sawmill. It was to carry out this work that the Women's Forestry Corps was formed. The Corps is a volunteer branch of the Land Army and gives to those young women who choose to join an interesting job and an insight into the working of the sawmilling industry. When the logs have been felled and the branches and tops lopped off, the girls measure the trunks with special tapes, mark them and prepare them for the lorries which take the timber off to the mills. At the mills themselves, the girls are usefully employed in measuring and sorting the converted timber as it emerges from the saw benches. When a piece of timber contains a large number of knots, it must be graded into a lower quality and put aside for uses where the presence of knots and defects does not impair its value. It is a full, open air life and already some 6,000 girls have voluntarily enrolled from the Land Army into the Forestry Branch. They live mostly in hostels and their welfare is closely watched over by

Virgin stands of white pine in Idaho, U.S.A.

Photo:

U.S. Forest Service.

Teak Tree in Burma, showing "girdling" at base before felling.

Photo:

Burma Teak Shippers.

Felling a noble fir tree with an electric felling machine in Washington, U.S.A.

Photo: U.S. Forest Service

Photo: T.D.A.

Natives felling hardwoods in West Africa

Tractor logging in Oregon, U.S.A.

Photo: U.S. Forest Service.

Elephants dragging teak logs in Burma.

Photo: Burma Teak Shippers.

Softwood logs in the ponds of a Swedish sawmill.

Raft of logs on the way down the Pacific Co
of Canada.

rain brings logs to dump in mill ponds
before conversion at Arkansas, U.S.A.

A teak raft, complete with natives' shack, on
a river in Burma.

Portable circular sawmill cutting pine in Alabama, U.S.A.

Photo: U.S. Forest Servic

Photo: T.D.A.

Converting a log flitch on a circular saw benc

ame saw cutting softwood logs in Sweden.

Photo: T.D.A.

to: U.S. Forest Service.

**Motor loader stacking converted lumber for
seasoning in mill yard, Idaho, U.S.A.**

Air view of a Swedish sawmill, with extensive
storage grounds alongside the quay.

Photo: Society for Cultural Relations with U.S.S.R.

Photo: T.D.

Port of Leningrad, U.S.S.R. Timber bei
loaded and awaiting shipment.

women inspectors; and questions of living conditions, wages or complaints against the managements about hours of work are all investigated by these welfare inspectors. There are still many other places in the sawmill where the girls can be useful, and the work has proved sufficiently attractive to induce hundreds of new recruits into the Corps during the last few months. There is plenty for all of them to do, and few jobs for women could be of greater benefit to the war effort than the aid they are giving to the production of the vast tonnage of timber used every day by a greedy industrial machine.

To augment the supply of labour, many sawmillers have been allocated squads of Italian prisoners and, although some of these men have naturally had no experience of the kind of work they now have to do, they are useful for the heavier tasks which cannot be carried out by women.

*   *   *   *   *   *

To give a clearer picture of the problems which had to be met in the expansion of British production, something should be said on the general set-up and organisation of these home mills. In this country, mills do not have the same machinery as those in Canada or the Soviet Union, for the raw material upon which they have to work is very different; yet the general principles governing the sawmill organisation are the same wherever the production is situated. Before the war, there were two types of mills over here. There was first of all the mill concerned primarily with the re-sawing of log timbers imported from the big producing countries, or the re-conversion of large dimension timber into the smaller sizes demanded by particular industries. Such mills had sets of saws specific in most cases to these functions, and many of them would have been incapable with the machinery at their disposal of converting English-felled logs to usable timber. The second class was made up of the mills dotted all over the countryside which did undertake the job of converting home felled logs. Much of their machinery was obsolete and in general their standard of competence was not impressive, with some notable exceptions. In any event, their daily output was ridiculously low in the majority of cases.

One result of being in "the doldrums" in peace time has been the very limited degree of mechanisation in English mills, although in the great producing countries, the conveyer belt and other mechanical aids to production are widely used. Over here, a volume of output was never reached which would have made these installations pay their way, and this lack of mechanisation has accentuated the labour problem considerably. Yet this rather primitive organisation is due not only to the fact that the industry could never support a highly industrialised structure because of its dwindling and insecure markets. Very many of the associated functions—and this applies equally to the bigger producers —lend themselves more readily to the individual touch of the hand of man than they do to the repetition of the machine. Timber grows—one

5

often hears this said by timbermen—it is a natural product and you cannot "manufacture" it in the same way as you manufacture steel or plastics. In the forests and in the mills, too, the human element is predominant. The feller—or faller—is now aided by automatic and power-driven saws, yet he takes his axe along with him on every job. The foreman has never been given a sorting robot which can pick out the bad from the good pieces as they emerge from the sawmill. They may come to him on a conveyer belt, but he must have his expert standing there to throw this one out, to pass this one as "prime"—at every stage the skilled knowledge of man must be employed directly without any of the mechanical "short-cuts" that have become customary in other industries.

The job of producing finished timber begins when the tree is felled in the wood or forest and, although the whole business does not sound very complicated, from the moment of felling until the trunk is transformed into usable timber, a great deal of work will have been carried out in the woods and mill. As soon as the logs are felled, the tops and branches must be lopped off and disposed of in accordance with their size and usefulness. The felling period is usually restricted to the winter months—and it is just in these months that the problems of transport are most difficult to solve. There is some difference of opinion as to why the winter months are chosen for felling, for many experts believe that spring and summer felling are equally satisfactory. The winter felling school will support their case by pointing out that in spring and summer the sap in the tree has risen from the base of the trunk and spread itself throughout the entire cell structure. The presence of this sap, they say, means not only that the tree dries very slowly when converted, but what is more serious, this sap contains all kinds of substances—starch, sugars, etc.—which make ideal food for fungi, and the sawn timber will very readily begin to rot as the fungi eat into the wood. The fact is that the sap is present in the cells of the tree at all times of the year, although during the months of growth—the spring and summer—the rate of flow is naturally greater. It is perfectly true that if logs are felled in spring or summer and left even for a short period before being converted, they are apt to be attacked by fungi and rot very rapidly. If for no other reason than this, winter felling is to be recommended.

The next problem is to get the logs from the woods to the sawmills. In many areas when the weather is mild, it is impossible to draw the logs out since the ground is so soft that the tractors cannot operate and the transport must wait until the frost hardens the ground. The logs are usually dragged out of the woods with the aid of a caterpillar tractor to some convenient spot where they can be loaded on to road or rail transport. If they go by road, a special route must be chosen where the lorry will meet the minimum of obstacles such as tight corners, low bridges and built-up areas generally. The handling of logs at the sawmills is always a problem since not every mill in this country has the necessary cranes or derricks to swing the bulky loads from the transport truck to the storage dump. If these facilities are not readily available it is a difficult job to get the logs safely piled away a reasonable distance from the saw bench, so that later on they can be manhandled and fed into the mill with the minimum of delay. The trees of the English woodlands are not very large in comparison with the Douglas fir or teak trees; nevertheless some of the hardwood stems may weigh anything up to five tons. The war time shortages of specially constructed lorries and experienced men have created many difficulties, for if the trunks are left too long in the woods, there is the danger of decay; or the farmer across whose fields the logs are to be dragged may have planted his corn and the way out is closed.

The sawmill has been part of man's equipment for many centuries and the earliest known mill—obviously a simple affair—was operated by the Greeks. The water wheel was used as the power unit some six hundred years ago when a mill was constructed at Augsburg; but there was no general adoption of mechanical sawing for some hundreds of years. Until the beginning of the nineteenth century, the pit saw was in general use in the producing areas and even today is still to be found in parts of Africa. It is operated by two men and the log to be sawn rests on the sides of the pit. The biggest development came with the invention of the circular saw, since this meant the end of man-operated saws and the introduction of the principle of continuous motion. The first record of its use is in the United States in the eighteen twenties and thenceforth it was rapidly adapted and used in sawmilling throughout the world; it is still an indispensable part of the equipment of the modern sawmill, although it is not the main instrument for log conversion in most up-to-date establishments.

The band saw—a long band of toothed steel strip—was a rather later development, and provides the basis for the majority of efficient sawmills in all producing countries. The band saw is in the form of an endless belt which cuts through the log as the steel band rotates. Sometimes these band saws are so arranged that the movement is vertical, whilst others have a horizontal action. A third type of saw is merely a variation of the band idea. It is called a frame saw and is, as its name implies, a frame in which are fitted a series of saws; the whole frame of saws moves backwards and forwards or up and down and cuts the log into boards as it goes.

In British mills, machinery of all kinds is to be found, but only the most efficient and modern mills are band mills. The log is loaded on to a flat platform and secured by steel dogs; this platform is the movable carriage which takes the log through the sawing process and is itself power-operated. It is the skill of the sawyer to set the log correctly on the carriage so that the conversion is economical and accurate. Much of the contents of a log can be lost by bad setting, and the problem is complicated by the fact that no log is ever truly cylindrical in shape or die straight in its length. If, for example, the log is bow-shaped and the saw is a horizontal one, it will probably be necessary to lay the log with the bow-shape flat to the carriage, otherwise the first few cuts that the saw takes will merely result in very short pieces, mainly bark and slabs, which have no use other than for stoking the boilers. Every time the carriage moves forward one plank of timber is cut so that in general the production by this method is slow. Time is spent in adjusting the log, and it may be that when about three-quarters of the log has been sawn to planks, the sawyer will release the dogs, turn the remaining segment over, secure it again and finish off the last few cuts. The skill of the sawyer is not only the speed at which he can accomplish all these functions efficiently; he must also have seen that his saw is the right kind for the wood he has to cut, that it is set correctly and that the tension on the steel strip is distributed over the width of the saw to give the right cutting edge. If the tension on the serrated edge is less than that of the outer edge, irregular cutting will result.

The frame saw—which can be likened in principle to the little gadget used for cutting hard-boiled eggs into slices—can produce more sawn timber per hour than the band mill, since at each operation the entire log can be sliced up into planks of the required thickness. It is, however, less accurate than the band mill, largely owing to the vibration which takes place as the set of saws work their way through the log. It has a further disadvantage in that the log cannot be shifted about to maximise the product produced, for once the saws have been set to the thicknesses required and the log sent forward on the carriage to engage the saws, there can be no interference until the whole log has been sawn up, by which time it is too late to vary the thickness of the planks in order to utilise the log more effectively. For some work, however, all these disadvantages are outweighed by the greater product per hour which a smoothly working frame saw can yield.

The construction of a frame or band mill is a major engineering project, for the whole machinery must be set in concrete and requires a large power unit to drive it. Space to move is also of the greatest importance in the laying out of a mill, for there must be sufficient room to move the larger and longer trunks which may have to be sawn. Some kind of crane, preferably an overhead gantry, should be installed as otherwise the heavier pieces cannot be handled rapidly by man power. There must be plenty of room, too, for piling the sawn timber so that it can season ready for use. Farther down the mill shop, there will probably be circular saw benches for "edging" the bark off the sawn planks and cross-cutting them to required lengths so that the final piece of timber which is piled away for seasoning will be the board or plank as it is known to the ordinary consumer.

The circular saw provides the third type of main machinery to be found in British mills and is perhaps the most common. Sometimes it is installed together with a band saw but in many cases it is the only conversion unit. The log is pushed against the revolving saw so that at each operation a board or plank of timber is cut off. It is not a very accurate method of production and rather wasteful, since the larger circular saws are so thick that they take out with each cut anything up to five-sixteenths of an inch; it can easily be calculated that the waste in sawdust is very high if, for example, one inch boards are being cut in this way. In some cases these saws are used merely to cut four slabs off the log and convert it into a large oblong (called a square), which can then be re-converted on a band re-saw into thinner material. The portable mills used on the site of the actual woods are of this type and have done valuable work during this war, since they eliminate the necessity of transporting a great deal of waste material which can be left in the woods. Such mills are a little primitive, but they have this advantage—they can be dismantled, packed on to a lorry and set up again on another site where there are plentiful supplies of logs upon which to work. The treed areas of Britain are in general so small that it seldom pays to erect a fixed mill alongside the woods unless that site has other favourable features such as good transport facilities, a cheap supply of power or proximity to the bigger consuming centres.

There are many different ways of cutting up the log, and each one is designed to meet the needs of some special work. The full explanation of all these methods is too detailed to be given here, but the reasons governing the use of these methods can in practice be put into two categories. In the first place, special conversion may be necessary in order to maximise one or more of the strength properties of the timber, for the structure of the tree is such that different surfaces of the cut timber will give different mechanical properties to the piece. Incidentally these various surfaces have different coefficients of contraction during seasoning, and special cutting may be employed to take advantage of this feature.

These strength properties are numerous, and not only do they usually vary when the same timber is cut in two different ways, but also each kind of tree has a dissimilar reaction to stresses applied to it. Thus the qualities called for in the timber used to hold up the floor of a small house are of a kind totally different from those needed to make a good pick-axe shaft. The other purpose of special cutting is to enhance the decorative value of the material; certain surfaces may exhibit a cell structure which is very beautiful, such as the light-coloured markings called "figure" which are sometimes to be found in oak panelling. It was discovered in the early days that if the round log was first cut into "quarters" making four irregular segments, then each of these "quarters" sawn again into boards, the surfaces of the sawn pieces would be covered with this attractive figure, particularly in the case of a few of the commoner hardwoods. Hence this method of conversion has become known as "quartering" a log, and many complicated variations have since been evolved. With all these methods of conversion, it is of paramount interest to the miller to see that he gets the largest possible product in the form of marketable timber of good dimensions.

When the log has been cut up into boards or planks, the material is carried to the drying stacks which are placed where the air can freely circulate between the piles and aid the seasoning process. The time taken to dry timber properly depends upon the thickness of the piece and the species; but the seasoning is usually a fairly lengthy process. Fully dried planks are required for most purposes whatever the manufacture, as drying which takes place after the wood has been made up into the finished article will certainly cause warping and probably result in splits and the forcing of joints. This question of drying has a particular importance in war time, since the majority of demands are so urgent that it might cause serious delay if the manufacturer has to wait six or eight months for his timber. Artificial drying has therefore taken the place of natural seasoning, and a large number of drying kilns are now being worked throughout the country. The use of these kilns demands a high standard of technical skill, for it is a very easy matter to ruin the timber by incorrect operation. The principle of all the processes— there are a number of different kinds of kilns—is to pass moist heat through the piles, gradually reducing the relative humidity of the kilning chamber until the timber is fully dried. The reason for keeping humidity fairly high is to avoid extracting the moisture at too quick a rate, since to do so would completely ruin the timber by breaking up the structure. In this branch of the industry there is room for research and development to perfect methods and educate users, for many believe the fallacy that the only effective seasoning is the natural, slow drying in the air. The reason for the persistence of these false ideas is that in the past the knowledge of artificial drying was so limited that much of the timber was in fact made useless by inexpert kilning. In normal times kilning was an expensive process and therefore not widely used, but in future it may be expected that new methods will reduce costs and extend its application. The greater knowledge which now exists as to the effects of humidity and temperature on cell structure will rapidly make air seasoning old-fashioned. In the modern industrial system, time has become a factor of considerable importance, and the development of kiln-drying will cut by many months the period taken to season timber of all kinds.

Some mention has already been made of the large percentage of waste which emerges when a log is converted and, in view of the new uses to which this waste material can be put, a little more may be said here on the subject. A tree in a forest is cut down and there is at once waste in the form of stump, branches and top. The cleaned length of trunk is then transported to the sawmill for conversion and the really heavy percentages of loss begin to appear. On an average some 13 per cent. can be written off at once for bark and a similar quantity for sawdust emerging during the process of conversion. The top slabs, edgings and trimmings account for a further 24 per cent., so that already half the original volume of the log has been dissipated. Losses due to careless manufacture and miscellaneous mistakes can account for a small percentage—say three. Finally, when the finished boards and planks are seasoning either in the air or kiln, shrinkage takes place during the drying process and a further 7 per cent. disappears. Thus from the

WASTE FROM LOG TO READY TIMBER

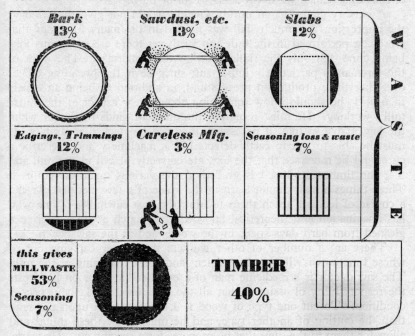

Bark
13%

Sawdust, etc.
13%

Slabs
12%

Edgings, Trimmings
12%

Careless Mfg.
3%

Seasoning loss & waste
7%

this gives
MILL WASTE
53%
Seasoning
7%

TIMBER
40%

WASTE

original log only some 40 per cent. is left in actual lumber—the balance has in part disappeared as in the case of the seasoning loss, or lies around the mill awaiting destruction. At least 37 per cent. of this material is usable—the sawdust, slabs, edgings and trimmings—since from it chemicals, cellulose, wood flour and a variety of other products could be produced. As it is, mountains of sawdust surround every big sawmill and the millers can do nothing but burn it, since no one will buy it and few will accept any even as a gift. The percentages given above will naturally depend upon the kind of sawmill, species of timber converted and the shape of the logs. The figures are averages computed on the basis of a survey of many operations made by the United States Forestry Service.

It must not be forgotten that on this 60 per cent. of waste material, the sawmiller will have expended labour charges and transport costs, so that if satisfactory uses could be found for these by-products it would sensibly affect the price of timber to the industrial consumer. To sell half of the waste at about the same price per ton as it cost the miller in the log would reduce the cost of the usable material by between one quarter and one third. In view of the developments in the employment of cellulose products for industrial purposes, here is a possibility for research which it would be in the public interest to pursue. The post-war world will hardly be able to afford the luxury of leaving these millions of tons of so-called waste products to rot or burn.

A cursory glance at an untidy sawmill would not give the stranger the impression that much skill was needed in the many functions that are being performed in the mill and yard; yet there are numerous jobs being done that only the skilled worker can undertake. The work of the foreman is particularly important, since he is the presiding officer over the whole production process and, in addition to being an expert in timber, he should know something about every aspect of the entire mill's working. He must recognise the different kinds of timber when the logs arrive so that, if necessary, they can be stacked separately; he must be able to run to earth defects in his machinery and prescribe a cure, and he must see that the logs are correctly placed in the mill and that the timber produced is graded to the various qualities required. These things a man cannot learn in the space of a few months, nor can a course of lectures teach them to him; the best sawmiller is one who has imagination and theoretical knowledge to match a wide experience gleaned from hard days spent in the woods and at the saw bench.

There are a number of other workers the proper carrying out of whose functions is vital to the efficient and speedy running of the mill. The saw doctor is a medicine man of a peculiar kind, for on him rests the responsibility of assuring that all the saws used are kept in proper condition. To cut one type of wood is a heavier strain upon the saws than the cutting of another type, and he must know these things and allow for them in the saws that he prepares for a specific cut. He works in his own shop, surrounded in modern mills by a whole array of complicated machinery, which automatically sharpens the saws to the required adjustment. He gives help and advice to the sawyer in the setting of the saws for the day's work. All this demands a lifetime of experience to bring it to perfection and an inefficient or unskilled saw doctor can easily ruin a set of saws or lower the standard of cutting of the sawmill.

What appears to be a very easy if strenuous job—the stacking of timber into neat piles for seasoning—is in fact one of the most difficult and can be put into the skilled category. It is here particularly that the shortage of labour has hit the sawmilling trade. With limited space, the untutored can easily pile so badly that the stacks are a danger to all who may have to pass by, and on a given piece of ground only a small percentage of the maximum load can be piled; in addition, no orderly unpiling will be possible when the timber is to be transported elsewhere to the site or factory. The men who used to perform these tasks at the big timber ports in peace time commanded high wages, since upon them devolved the correct stacking of a given quantity on the land available in conformity with all the regulations in existence governing safety, fire avoidance and in such a manner that the timber if emerging wet from the ship's hold did not rot in the piles and be valueless when unpiled. The speed at which they worked was extraordinary, and an average man would stand aghast and watch the loads their sturdy shoulders carried up a narrow plank from the water's edge to the top of a pile.

The man, armed with a rule, thick blue crayon and small duplicate book, who measures and marks the cut timber as it emerges from the mill has the job of measuring rapidly and accurately and calculating correctly. On the basis of the pages of his little book specifications are prepared which give the user a piece by piece list of the timber he has purchased and shows how much he owes his timber merchant. All these workers have an important part to play in the sawmill organisation, and there are others whose skill is less but whose activities are just as necessary to keep the machinery going and the timber moving from lorry to mill, from mill to stack, from stack to factory.

* * * * * *

These are the main problems of the industry—the felling and transportation of the logs, the milling of the timber and the correct and rapid seasoning prior to use. It was just these problems which the authorities had to face when they started, somewhat belatedly, to step up home production: but the full story of this development must wait until hostilities cease. Something can, however, be said of the action that was taken to meet the very great demands for home-produced timber.

For the first few months of the war when the general policy everywhere was that "time was on our side", practically nothing was done to stimulate home production and no effective provisions in the original schemes covered this side of the timber supply position. The mills that did exist were able to carry on in their usual slow manner with a slight increase in output, but the regulations imposed by the Ministry of Supply did not stipulate that home-produced timber was to be used; in addition, there were reasonable quantities of imported timber available, and few troubled to look ahead and realise the situation that was going to arise as soon as the U-boat war entered into its more destructive phase. Many warnings were issued, but the only positive action was the imposition of maximum prices on milled timber to prevent any profiteering. These prices were reasonably profitable, but many of them were unfortunately higher than those of the better imported material, and while the supply of such stock was being maintained, there was obviously no inducement to the war industries to ask for the lower graded home-produced article. Later on, when the production of home-grown timber had been stepped up considerably, the millers lost again, for they found that the supplies of softwood logs were difficult to obtain and the logs themselves small and wasteful, so that once more the prices were unprofitable. Many mills, with some experience of bad times, went through a period when they were unable to sell their production, and only a few private individuals and firms could foresee the enormous demand for their products that was shortly to emerge. These people went around the country—and credit is due to them for their foresight—buying up land and forests, mills and premises ready for the day when the U-boat would force Britain to consume the wood from the trees of her own countryside. Others estimated the situation correctly and invested their capital in new machines, and sawmills began to spring up near most forest areas and in the big towns. This was still at a time when the demand was low and a large number of producers were working at well under maximum output. There was then no shortage of logs and throughout the country piles of felled trees could be seen, awaiting the saw. Many skilled men could not be regarded in the circumstances as vital to the war effort, and they were released to the services or to what were considered to be more important branches of industry.

Such a ridiculous situation could not really last for very long, although it was perhaps in keeping with the attitude current throughout the country at that time. The U-boat began its destructive drive against British shipping, and hundreds of thousands of tons of valuable ships and cargoes went to the bottom of the Atlantic in a very short space of time. Shipping tonnage for the bulky timber cargoes began to be less and less frequent, and stocks tumbled down as the industrial demand started to rise in sympathy with the production spurt which followed Dunkirk, and it looked as if there would soon be no imported timber available for anyone. The small interest in the home output shown by the authorities appears in retrospect little short of fantastic. There was a department of the Ministry of Supply responsible for the activities of the mills, but in spite of the suggestions of many well-meaning people who mooted everything from telescoping to State control, the peace time pace had hardly increased in the first year of the war.

At the eleventh hour the Ministry acted, and the mills that had been silent for so long began to roar away as they slashed the tree trunks; those that had been on half-time now began to work overtime to keep pace with the rush of requirements, and machinery was imported from America to increase output at the earliest possible moment. Although much of this new machinery was of inefficient design, unsuited to the work on the English trees, production did race ahead, and a special department of the Ministry was set up to look after the home production. In its scope came questions of labour, transport and raw material—in fact anything cognate to the problem of producing more and more timber at a quicker and quicker rate. The home trade was taken a little by surprise by this sudden interest in its activities, since for twenty-five years it had remained forgotten. There was as a result reluctance in some quarters to take the new development seriously and a not unreasonable suspicion that as soon as the temporary need had been met, the industry would once again be left more or less in the lurch to fight an uphill battle against the flood of cheap imports from every country in the world. But production grew and went on growing. Those who had shown foresight in their investments in mills and standing timber were able to be of real service to the nation in an hour of extreme need. The normal peace time percentage of consumption met by home production was doubled and then trebled in as short a space of time so that the problems now to be faced were no longer questions of idle machinery, halftime labour and piles of logs. Machinery was insufficient and inspectors were sent out to see how a particular plant could be made to step up production in the shortest possible time. Labour became scarce and a new drive to get sufficient semi-skilled workers was put in hand; the Essential Works provisions protected existing staffs, but did not help in the nation-wide problem of increasing the total labour force available to the industry. Producers who had so recently been beggars after work became unwilling to take on more while they had six months' commitments to meet. Transport of all kinds presented a puzzle which if unresolved promised to nip in the bud the entire advantage of the new production spurt. A certain number of timber transport vehicles were made available to the industry, and with the help of regional pooling schemes and all the other dodges of war-time economy the worst effects of shortage of facilities were avoided But the saws went on producing, the stocks piled up, the war industries. received the supplies they needed and the home producers were at last able to play their true part in that terrific industrial recovery which saved the country from obliteration, and made possible the successful offensives so soon to surprise the world—offensives which in 1940 seemed the most unlikely thing that could happen.

The problems that had beset the industry twelve months before were soon forgotten but a new set emerged which were even more difficult to solve. Britain, partly as a result of the unrestricted felling of trees in the 1914-18 War, is not well supplied with suitable timber, and this great spurt of production used up very large quantities of the available trees. Search was made in every corner of the country for timber, and it must be ruefully recorded that in certain places there was considerable opposition from landowners to the felling of their trees. There developed a kind of underground sabotage to which reference has already been made and, although in total it had small effect upon the final result, it came at a time when every fellable tree was urgently needed by a war factory. Some people objected because they always do object to being told what is expected of them; others because they placed the beauty of some ancient park above the interests of a nation fighting for its existence. One large landowner refused to allow his avenue of trees to be felled because they were planted to commemorate the Coronation of George IV, and he considered it was in the "National interest" that such an asset should be retained for the future. His park was not, of course, open to the general public, so that the enjoyment of this fine avenue of stately stems was restricted to a rather select body of the nation. However, as an answer, it was probably thought that it would do, and those who preferred fewer trees to more Nazis had an uphill struggle against this kind of gentry. Powers did exist in the hands of the authorities to requisition such estates but these powers were used, as customary, in very few cases and only where the breach of national interests was particularly flagrant. It should be added that there were many who were ready at any time to let the nation have all it wanted from their estates. Today the restrictions have been tightened up, and in any event it is unusual to find owners offering strong resistance to an order to fell or a request to purchase their standing timber. The country is divided into divisions, over each of which a divisional officer presides and if there are any objections, this officer can make a full investigation. The felling is carried out unless such objections are found to fall justifiably within one of the following five categories:—

    i. A high proportion of the timber on the estate has already been disposed of.
    ii. The trees are essential shelter or necessary for agricultural purposes.
    iii. The trees are of high botanical or silvicultural importance.
    iv. The trees have a definite and proved amenity value.
    v. That the owner has some special objection to the purchaser who wishes to acquire the trees.

The axe has fallen in many of Britain's beauty spots and it will take decades to fill some open space or heal an ugly sore; but lovers of the green countryside can take comfort from the knowledge that a reasonable plan now exists to control felling of all trees. Those who wish to fell must first obtain sanction from the Ministry to exploit the site, and in granting such permits the authorities are careful to see that the timber to be cut is used to the best possible advantage. Some forests and woodlands contain a number of trees ideally suited for the production, for example, of pit-props for the mines—a most valuable article in war-time Britain—and it is the job of the officials to see that those trees are directed to that particular use. This avoids using timber for consumption of minor importance, for in war of all times, there are definite priorities to be observed in the utilisation of raw materials.

Today the position is vastly different from that of the early war years when very little had been done to stimulate home production. The figures of output are, of course, not published, but it has been stated officially that something like two-thirds of total consumption is made up from home sources. If this figure is correct, it is a triumph indeed for the home industry, since it must not be forgotten that the industry is, by its energetic efforts now, destroying the hope of a really plentiful supply of raw material for after war purposes. This is a consideration which naturally should never enter the heads of those whose job it is to obtain the nation's timber supply; nevertheless it is gratifying to see that traders who have co-operated in making the programme a reality have not let post-war considerations stand in the way of maximum output. Not all industries can say the same, and certainly other branches of the timber trade have spent too much time and energy in arguing over questions of Government remuneration for the small distributive functions that they undertake.

The home timber traders have made a maximum contribution to the war effort, and all the while they have been conscious of the fact that the very life-blood of their future industry was being drained away with every new estate that fell to the axe. The Ministry itself established a few departmental mills and these were at first regarded as direct competitors in the industry and represented, some believed, a threat to the after war freedom of the trade. But the peace was maintained because these State mills are very few in number and only work upon the raw material which most of the ordinary mills will not use.

The production targets set have now been reached, and the output is continuing to rise to such a level that a very appreciable saving in shipping space has been made during the last eighteen months. The labour force has expanded so that today it is about seven times as large as it was at the outbreak of war, and with the continued recruitment of women workers this rise can go on. As the authorities have themselves admitted, some damage has been done both to the structure of the home industry and to the countryside by this necessary felling and production. The damage to the industry is no more than that which many other sections of the public have had to endure in the fight; that they have borne it so willingly and co-operated so energetically is in keeping with the needs of this total war. The damage to the countryside is not irreparable, but it will take time to heal the sores and fill the empty spaces that have appeared all over the United Kingdom, but particularly on the woody slopes of Scotland. The extent to which the land is once more covered with young trees depends upon the way this problem is tackled in the era of post-war reconstruction. Something will be said later on the plans that have so far been announced for post-war forest policy; but those who fear that there will be no trees at all left to beautify the countryside need not worry. There are very many trees now adorning the hedgerows and fields which will never be suitable for conversion even in war time. There are elms, oaks and poplars which are too rough grown to be of much use; and in many districts neglect of the trimming and care of the tree have made it impossible to use it in the sawmill. Ivy is one of the scourges of the English woodlands for, although some ivy-covered elm tree may look very charming, that ivy has stifled the growth of the tree and made it useless for timber. In many places the soil is too wet and the trees only grow to a certain age before they die; it is to be hoped that in the future it will be possible to refrain from planting in such areas so that the hundreds of dead or half dead trees which now disfigure the countryside in some counties will disappear for ever.

In the great development which has gone on in the last three years not all the items are debits, for something of permanent value has been learnt both in methods of sawmilling and silviculture. A large number of people now have a detailed knowledge of the problems of the sawmill, and experts have been trained who will be able to put their accumulated experience to good purpose after the war. The vices and virtues of a range of hitherto unused native timbers have been discovered in the hard war years, and it should be possible to advise the Forestry Commission or that body which is charged with the re-planting of Britain's trees what are the best kinds of trees to grow to meet the industrial demand. Experiments—some of them painful for the pioneers—have been made with numerous machines, and it should not be difficult to assess the values of the various types of mills for the conversion of home-felled logs. Many timbermen who had grown accustomed to dealing with one or two different imported timbers and could not distinguish a Corsican pine from a larch now possess experience of identification more extensive than anything they had before, and they will be eager to extend their knowledge of the woods that they handle, their strength properties, their nature and the best way to cut them. The results will be of permanent advantage both to society and to the industry that these men control, since there will be a greater willingness on their part to meet in the proper scientific manner the competition of substitute materials and give to the using public the best possible advice. A great deal of the substitution which has gone on in the last fifty years was not due to any inherent defectiveness of timber as a material for the work in question; it was rather that those who were responsible for producing and marketing timber did not display the same technical abilities as their steel, concrete or plastics rivals in analysing their products scientifically and occupying the vanguard of industrial developments. The scope is unlimited, for whereas the steel producer need only be a metallurgist and a mechanic, the efficient timberman must be a botanist, a chemist, an expert on mechanical properties, a sawmiller, and have a working knowledge of fireproofing, kiln drying and how to deal with the many parasites and fungi which attack timber if allowed to do so.

Here, indeed, are opportunities for human activity promising enough to attract the most ambitious, sufficiently vast to engage the attention of the gifted scientist and the technician. The future road of timber technology is without end for those who have the courage to travel it.

"In a word, so astonishing and wonderful is the organisms, parts and functions of plants and trees; as some have, as we said, attributed animal life to them, and that they were living creatures; for so did Anaxagoras, Empedocles, and even Plato himself.

"I am sure plants and trees afford more matter for medicine, and the use of man, than either animals and minerals, or any exotic we have besides; are more familiar at hand, and safe; and within this late age wonderfully improved, increased and searched into, and seems by the Divine wisdom, to be an inexhaustible subject for our disquisition and admiration.

"There are ten thousand considerations more, besides that of their medicinal and sanative properties, and the mechanical uses mentioned in this treatise, which a contemplative person may derive from the groves and woods; all of them the subject of wonder: And though he had only the palm, (which Strabo affirms is fit for three hundred and sixty uses,) or the coco, which yields wine, bread, milk, oyl, sugar, vinegar, tinctures, tanns, spices, thread, needle, linnen, and cloth, cups, dishes, spoons, and other vessels and utensils; baskets, mats, umbrellas, paper, brooms, ropes, sails, and almost all that belongs to the rigging of ships. In short, this single tree furnishing a great part of the world with all that even a voluptuous man can need, or almost desire; it were sufficient to employ his meditations and his hands, as long as he were to live, though his years were as many as the most aged oak."

JOHN EVELYN: *Sylva*

CHAPTER III

WOOD IN WAR AND PEACE

WOOD IS so much a part of everyday life that its great importance to a modern industrial society is often overlooked. It is generally easy to obtain, simple to use or treat, and in a thousand applications it enjoys pride of place. At times alternatives are produced which in some respects are an improvement upon timber for a specific job, and such substitution is a daily feature of a changing industrial system. Despite this fact, the consumption of timber continues to increase year by year against the ever-watchful competition of metals of all kinds, plastics and a host of new synthetic materials that man's ingenuity contrives to invent.

In the days before this war, one of the most, if not the most, extensive consumers of wood was the building and construction industry, and to this use went many thousands of standards of timber of every kind. Indeed, to a very great extent the prosperity of the timber trade of this country depended upon the ups and downs of small house building, because not only is there timber in the construction of the villa itself but for practically every piece of furniture put into the house, timber will be needed in its manufacture. New trends in interior decorative methods usually seem to call for more and not less timber. Parquet floors, the re-birth of the panelled room and the shingle roofing of some kinds of modern house, all contributed to demand more and more wood from Britain's suppliers across the seas. Most of this timber came from the Scandinavian countries, Finland, Russia, and, after the Ottawa Conference, big quantities were sent from the Dominion of Canada.

It is impossible to list the numerous uses to which this easily acquired raw material was put. Motor-cars were partly of timber, bridge construction called for heavy timbers, thousands of wooden packing cases took Britain's exports to the world's markets. Furniture, boxes, coffins, silos, ships and boats, matches, refrigerators, pavements, brushes, aeroplanes, rifle butts, bobbins—the list is unending, and from the cradle to the grave the average man is daily in contact with something made of wood. Very roughly, the main uses for wood and timber were building and construction work, railway, motor and vehicle construction, boxes and crates, furniture, paper and cardboard, and a variety of general articles best described as "woodware". Together these uses accounted for a very big percentage of the total consumed. One use which was not of great importance in this country in peace time but which other nations have developed into a formidable industry, was the extraction of various chemicals from wood or wood pulp and on this subject more will be said later.

The outbreak of war brought radical changes in the use to which it was possible to put timber, and here it is proposed to mention only the main changes which eventually followed the outbreak of war and the subsequent measures of economic control which it became necessary to take. One of the first acts of the Government was to stop building and construction work, unless, of course, such work was in connexion with a factory or some other approved war enterprise. From the exigencies of war there emerged a new and somewhat strange body of timber consumers. The Civil Defence authorities required timber for the vast programme of A.R.P. work which was only completed well after the war began, and later on blitzed areas needed to rebuild parts of their towns or make safe those that had been badly damaged. Engineers and contractors turned at once to timber and grasped eagerly at anything they could lay their hands on to meet the urgent needs of the moment. Shelters were propped up with timber, houses re-conditioned or at least made habitable, basements were strengthened with timber and steel and finally thousands of bunks appeared in every shelter throughout the country, most of which were framed in wood.

The Army, through its appropriate purchasing department of the whole supply system, began to call for enormous quantities, not only to be used in the manufacture of the things it needed such as tanks, guns, trucks and so on, but also for actual operations, for bridging, for housing its rapidly increasing numbers, for a thousand different jobs which it would be impossible to mention. Perhaps the biggest single need was for hutting; and throughout the country one can see with one's own eyes the vast quantities of timber that have gone to give shelter to the armed forces. In some instances there have been particularly interesting developments in its use which will only become obvious to the curious eyes of the public when hostilities cease; but all can see the huts and many can see the piles of rejected packing cases that often lie around near big Army centres. Each packing case used to carry the Army's requirements has been cut from some tree, British or imported, and if it is the latter has had to compete for freight space against what appear to be the far more important items of guns, tanks, shells or planes. But a valuable piece of equipment which is sent, for example, from Scotland to the South Coast, must have a stout packing case of timber, otherwise it will almost certainly be damaged in transit and on arrival at a distant destination prove useless.

When some new operation commences, the Army's demand for timber of all kinds jumps violently upwards, and again every small piece has to be found either from the stocks of home woods or brought over in the ships that are so badly needed for other cargoes. During the last war in the years 1915 and 1916 about 14 million tons dead weight of shipping were used to bring in the timber required for all purposes, and, by the way, the cost of this timber was enormously greater than the pre-1914 figure. Of this grand total, Army requirements represented a very large proportion. The main reason was, of course, the existence of a long front based upon trench warfare; and to carry this front timber was required in the rear areas as well as for trench supports and buttressing, duck-boards and shelter roofs. A push by the enemy and an Allied retreat of a few furlongs probably meant that the entire system of trenches and communications in that part of the front had to be reconstructed. More timber was therefore required from the back areas and, although France herself did magnificent things in providing a great proportion of this need, the demand was so great that no one country could have supplied it all. This was an expensive type of warfare from the timber point of view; but there is no evidence to show that the present warfare is any less prodigal in its consumption of timber. In addition to the requirements of Britain's armed forces, quantities of arms have been packed and shipped to other Allied countries. All these shipments called for timber in one form or another, and in fact it was said at one time that the quantity of packing timber used in shipping to the Soviet people the arms, tanks and planes they have used so effectively was greater than the amount of ordinary Russian timber that Britain was receiving from the Russians; Britain was, in fact, exporting timber to one of the greatest timber producing countries in the world! The North African campaign is another example of an operation calling for the employment of timber in enormous quantities. Hundreds of ships were used in that operation, and each one had to have its hold battened or platforms placed to take tanks and armoured cars, not to mention the numbers of erstwhile luxury liners and freighters that were hastily converted to carry the troops. These conversions, whilst leaving the main parts of the ship intact, alter the accommodation considerably and partitions for mess rooms, sick bays, refrigerators, armouries and even the ship's "glass house," are usually reconstructed from wood and plywood.

The occupation of new areas by our armies again calls for timber and, although some of the material may be on the spot, there are areas such as North Africa which always were in peace time large importers of timber from the South European countries. This has meant that from Britain or direct from across the Atlantic military and civil requirements of newly acquired territories must be met and, although the normal demands will not operate, the new forces need to be housed and supplied with all the manifold requirements of a modern army. Every shell that is fired, every bomb that is dropped and every tin of bully that is eaten will have arrived packed in a timber box or crate. Some of the boxes that contain delicate mechanisms connected with shell, bombs or special devices such as depth charges are themselves very strong and complicated constructions in wood. This is essential to avoid any friction or damage where highly explosive materials are to be packed, and some of these packings are today being made by the skilled cabinet makers of the pre-war years. Some of those who are now helping to pack a 4.7 shell safely were before artistically copying Sheraton or following the arts of the woodcarvers.

Large as is the demand from the various branches of the Army, the Navy and its ancillary service, the Merchant Navy, run the Army close in the quantity that they consume. Some of the most interesting and revolutionary applications of wood material have taken place in the ship and boatbuilding industries where timber has always been one of the primary raw materials. It is many decades since ships were built from the ancient and gnarled oaks of Kent, Sussex and the other forest lands of Britain, and whilst there has been no attempt, because of shortage, to emulate the feats of the Elizabethan shipbuilders, a number of very excellent craft built entirely of wood have been developed. These range from plywood and all-wood lifeboats and barges to the bigger type of minesweeper. Some publicity has already been given both in this country and in Canada to the so-called "pocket destroyer", otherwise the Fairmile boat, which is a moderate sized craft built entirely of timber, and is now an important part of our coastal defences, and has proved of particular value not only because of its speed and armament for a boat of its size, but mainly because it can be mass produced at an incredible rate. The excellent achievements of Mr. Henry J. Kaiser on the Pacific Coast in the building of Liberty ships from steel are equalled in some respects by the production of these pocket destroyers. Here, too, the scheme was the idea of one man, and it is to his credit that even before hostilities commenced he was pressing the Admiralty to consider the proposition in the event of war. There were many vicissitudes before the boats began to roll from the assembly points, but now they are coming off at such a rate that it is difficult to keep pace with the timber supplies that they need. Their advantages are in the lightness of construction, and it is noticed that they suffer less from underwater explosions than the more rigid, stronger steel-built craft. Many a pocket destroyer has distinguished itself in action off the coast of enemy-occupied territory, and they will play an even greater part in the operations of the future. A fair proportion of the timber used is grown in this country and such advances have been made in substitution that in the case of many other small craft, the construction is entirely from timbers grown within the United Kingdom.

It is not only the pocket destroyer that is built from the timbers of the forests. There are a whole variety of small boats, motor torpedo craft, motor boats, lifeboats and ships boats generally that are now, and a few of them have been for some time, built from wood. But the war has naturally led to an increase in building which has made heavy demands upon Britain's timber supplies.

The boatbuilder has not found it easy to make his ways fit in with the new supply conditions. The majority were old craftsmen who had spent their lifetime in the boatyards, making cabin cruisers or ships boats from the finest timbers that commerce could bring. The teak of Burma, the mahogany of Honduras, the Southern pine from the Gulf Ports were their raw materials. Today they have to use the cheaper woods and produce at a rate which was unknown to them in the past. In general they have succeeded in rising to the occasion, and a continual stream of small craft emerge to be manned by the tough young sailors who have something of the Drake tradition in their daring as they dart in and out of enemy concentrations, damaging, sinking and scattering the enemy. It is upon their superior craft, seamanship and courage that they depend to carry the day.

Many other craft now taking part in defensive or offensive operations are mainly built from the materials of the woods and forests. An important type of minesweeper is largely of wood construction and timber plays a very big part in the construction of other medium sized ships such as trawlers. In shipbuilding proper, timber is used more as part of the equipment of production rather than of the ship itself. In the case of large naval combat vessels, the main construction is, of course, in steel, but internal fittings are in many cases of wood, although the combustibility of the material has limited its use in those places where fire is a grave danger. All the timber that is put into combat vessels is

fireproofed and, although the process of proofing does not prevent the
wood from burning in the event of a general conflagration, it limits
considerably the combustibility of the timber and renders it less likely
to ignite in the event of being struck, for example, by red hot shell
splinters. In heavy ships, such as battleships and cruisers, it is necessary
to use wooden decks in order to insulate below decks for service in all
climates.   Such decking is usually of teak or a Borneo wood called
Serayah: but the occupation by the Japanese of the areas from which
both these timbers are produced has led to the consideration of
substitutes.

The shipyards use large quantities of timber for the production and
launching of the vessels. The staging planks and uprights, which are
the scaffolding surrounding the hull during construction, are all timber,
and in the case of the latter much of it has for many years come from
the woodlands of the North of England and Scotland. Wedges, blocks
and parts of the slipway are of wood and the joinery shops of a large
shipyard have a hundred and one uses for timber.

In the building of a freighter, the construction equipment is similar,
and here, too, in the ship itself very little wood is wanted; hatch covers,
internal sheathing, joinery work and miscellaneous equipment are the
main timber parts. The merchant shipyards tend to use less and less
timber as the construction becomes more rapid and modern methods
replace the older and slower ones. There will, however, always be a
certain amount required in the ship itself and for such ancillary work
as patterns, shipyard plant and ships boats.

All these changes in the kind of use to which timber was put came
slowly as the war developed and factories turned over their woodworking machinery to uses more in line with the Government's demands.
There were many specialists in woodwork who preferred to convert
their production to light metal articles and use their particular kind of
skill and machinery on aeroplane and similar small engineering products.
With few exceptions, the industry has changed over to meet the new
requirements, and it has been surprising to watch the extent to which
the needs of war can be met from the wheels that have for decades
turned in the service of the arts of peace. A particularly significant
development has been in the progress made in "near-timber" products
by the extension of the synthetic wood ideas embodied in plywood and
plastics.

The aircraft industry has always displayed a keenness in research
and development which might be copied by other industries; and in
this war, credit is due to the Ministry of Aircraft Production for the
way in which it has used many of the new ideas on methods and materials
presented to it. Wood has been for many years a raw material of the
aircraft producers not only here but in many other countries. It will be
remembered that some amusement was occasioned when on Mussolini's
special plea to Hitler, Italian planes were "permitted" to take part in

raids on this country during the great *blitz* of 1940. One air battle took place in which an entire squadron of Italian planes was shot out of the sky by Spitfires and Hurricanes of Fighter Command, and it was pointed out that the few planes which fell on British soil undamaged were constructed almost entirely of wood. They had, it was said at the time, very little chance against the all-metal fighters that Britain was then beginning to build in large numbers. This was only partly true, for although the Italian fighters were quite incapable of meeting Spitfires and Hurricanes in combat, this was because they were obsolete types and aerodynamically years behind the British machines. It was nothing to do with the materials of which they were made. For witness the growth and success of the all-wood plane—the Mosquito—which has proved itself not only as an effective long-range fighter, but also as a formidable light bomber which so far no German fighter can catch in normal conditions.

At all times, wood has been used to a limited extent in aircraft. Sitka spruce from the Pacific Coast of Canada was at one time the main material for certain types and ash was used in some others. Today both these woods are employed together with plywood in the construction of the Mosquito. Spruce and mahogany have also provided the material for airscrews, but the use of timber for this purpose fell from favour at the beginning of the war only to be revived quite recently, and this reversal is an eloquent tribute to the part that trees have played in a war of steel and machines.

The employment of timber in various forms in aircraft dates from the development of two new discoveries in industrial processes. The first was the introduction of plywood manufacture, which is merely the sticking together of very thin sheets of wood so that maximum strength is achieved with minimum weight. To obtain these thin sheets, which are sometimes only one-hundredth of an inch thick, logs of timber were immersed for a period in water and then sliced up on a machine resembling a large bacon cutter. For other purposes "rotary cut" veneers or sheets are used, and these are made by rotating the log against a very sharp knife edge so that the whole log is, as it were, "unrolled" into one long, continuous sheet of veneer. The production of such veneers opened up an enormous field of new possibilities, and it is in the construction of aircraft that these developments have been most striking.

The second feature, which hinges on the production of plywood, was the discovery and use of glues of such composition and strength that the synthetic board of several veneers was as durable and as strong as or stronger than the solid wood itself. Something more will be said on the question of glues later on; here it can be mentioned that the new types of synthetic resin glues are plastic glues of great durability, able to withstand chemical changes as well as immersion in water and wide variations in temperature.

In the early days of aircraft, timber was naturally regarded as a suitable material and later on plywood played its part for wings and fuselage. Both materials began to lose favour on account of the difficulties encountered in gluing the members together. The glues that were used in those days were often attacked by fungi which enjoyed the food value of the glue, and it is said that some of the planes so constructed in the last war grew "mushrooms" on their wings from this cause. This difficulty has been overcome and now plywood and timber have come to stay as airplane materials. They have several very interesting advantages which will make them of importance in peace as well as war-time aircraft. Timber properly selected and prepared can have far greater rigidity than steel of the same size and weight; in addition pound for pound wood members can be loaded with a greater weight before they deflect than can metal. Wood absorbs vibration much more effectively than metal, andthese three qualities combine to produce a superior material for modern construction. In a large bomber there may be as many as 450,000 rivets, and their presence creates a drag which must be eliminated to give maximum speed. The use of plywood enables parts of the plane to be moulded in one piece and thus provide a stream-lined member unbroken by these thousands of rivets. Two further advantages emerge in active service conditions; repairs can more easily be carried out on a plywood section and when the plane is attacked, bullets pass cleanly through the wood instead of tearing a jagged hole as in the case of a bullet through metal.

New developments in the production of plastics for plane construction have been made in the United States and, although very little information is available as to their manufacture, it is known that they are all based upon a process of compressing wood, or its derivative paper, into a homogeneous mass which is capable of bearing very great stresses at all temperatures likely to be met. Already in this country the solid timber and metal construction of propeller blades has been replaced in some cases by this plastic material.

These new uses, particularly in the case of aircraft, have been due largely to the application of accumulated knowledge to material research, rather than to the discovery of anything new in materials themselves. Thus the multi-layer plywood fuselage built up on the Mosquito is considered by many to be stronger than the previous metal construction for similar work. Novel methods of combining and strengthening timber layers or plies have created new strength properties which were considered previously to be the monopoly of the light alloys. Each has an important part to play in industrial development and just as the light alloys were important because they brought new features of weight and strength to metal construction, discoveries of methods of treating or breaking down the timbers of the world will provide industry with novel products. Every day, particularly during the stress of war, many experiments are being carried out on substitute materials and as the knowledge of wood structure grows, so it will become not just one of the most used and least understood raw products, but an up-to-date basis for many purposes to be treated, combined, tested and prepared to meet a demand at present regarded as outside its normal scope.

It must be remembered that it is not only the much advertised Mosquito which is of wood construction. This plane is important since it is the only first line operational aircraft at present constructed entirely of wood, but for a considerable time many other non-operational planes have been entirely or partly of wood construction. The Canadian Anson V is almost wholly of wood construction and in numerous others, particularly those now being built in the huge new Canadian factories, wood plays a vital part in providing the material for frames and screws.

Many operational machines have a number of parts made from wood or wood plastics. The Consolidated B-24, better known as the Liberator, has more than twenty such parts and the use of wood saves about 205 pounds weight of aluminium alloys. Trimming tabs, guards for control rods, control knobs, · aileron quadrants, gunners' doors and escape hatches are but a few of the plastic wood parts on this high performance bomber. It is hoped that wing tips, which measure about three feet by four-and-a-half feet, will soon be of similar construction, and experiments are now being carried out with other parts which should show a saving both in weight and cost.

Apart from the war-time uses on trainers, gliders and for parts of operational machines, there is a possibility of employing these new methods on the construction of massive cargo planes which are designed to carry a somewhat different load ratio. It may not be possible to dispense with metal altogether, but the present line of development which has been so greatly extended because of the urgent needs of war, can produce civil planes at a much lower price by the correct combination of metal and wood plastics. The American Consolidated Company with their C-87 cargo plane are carrying on experiments on this joint production basis.

The peace time value of timber as a material vital to the building of the small house has been mentioned; this particular employment is no longer of great importance while the war lasts. The needs of war have, however, created a new demand for heavy timber in the construction of factories, hangars, and every kind of war plant and establishment. Great things have been done and timber has been used where before it was regarded as an unsuitable material. The main reasons for the reversal to this type of construction were in the first place the acute shortage of the chief constructional material—steel. Priority demands for steel in America and this country for tanks, cars, shells and a thousand other articles of war, made it impossible to spare any quantity for structural work. In America particularly the availability of timber caused its immediate employment to meet the steel shortage, although in this country the long distances over which the timber has to be hauled has tended to limit its use considerably. In cost there is very little to choose between the two in the United States and labour can be saved by factory pre-fabrication of parts. A second sound reason for the use of timber was the existence of a fund of woodworking labour. Steel workers, whether of the engineering or civil construction categories, were rapidly and readily absorbed into the vast new armament plants which began to operate from 1941 onwards. But woodworkers found only a limited scope for their activities and the introduction of the timber heavy construction at once made a demand upon their services—and which is as important, there were enough of them to handle the work both in the factories producing the pre-fabricated parts and on the job assembling the wooden members.

New wonders of civil engineering and construction have emerged from the needs of war and many of them will have taught lessons, the results of which will be apparent long after the guns have ceased to roar. There were difficulties to be overcome such as the rendering of the buildings reasonably fireproof and the control of rot and termites, but these problems have been solved and a system of concrete and timber is growing up to replace the scarce steel. After the war, the immense demand for new buildings will enable timber to make its contribution to the reconstruction in every country hit by the war and new avenues of research and development will open up before the eyes of those responsible for recreating the permanence and beauty of towns and villages, places of worship and entertainment.

In the past, two of the deciding factors in using wood for heavy constructional work have been the greater fire risk and the shorter life due to the attacks of fungi and other forms of rot. Here, too, the war has seen great steps forward which will make heavy timbers real competitors of steel in the future. Fire or flame proofing methods have been known for centuries, and the Romans used to dip their timber in vinegar or a solution of alum more than two thousand years ago. Untreated wood matter generally will ignite at about 600 degrees Fahrenheit, whereas steel loses its strength and concrete begins to break up at about 1,000 degrees. These figures are significant when it is considered that the temperature of a burning building is between 1,300 and 1,700 degrees Fahrenheit. In the case of large timbers, the strength is retained for long periods, since the charred outer wood retards further combustion and will often preserve the structure until the fire is obliterated by outside means or burns itself out. A reduction of combustibility may be achieved by two methods; one way is to impregnate the wood with fire-retarding chemicals and the other to apply special paint so that the wood presents a resistant surface to the flame. The former is the more efficacious method and a number of chemicals have been used as fireproofing liquids, the most common of which is ammonium phosphate. Firms here and in America have patented processes which give very good performances. All these chemicals do not prevent charring but they reduce very considerably flaming and smouldering, and further research may be expected to result in an even greater degree of efficiency.

Preservative treatment can also be successfully applied to limit the chances of rot in timber, and every year new chemical processes are evolved which make the protection more effective. The life of timber members has now been greatly increased by these means, and there is reason to hope that the post-war constructor can use timber properly treated in the knowledge that its strength will not be impaired by rot within a reasonable period.

One of the most outstanding achievements in the heavy type of construction was recently disclosed in the United States where a permanent naval hangar, built to house some of the U.S. Navy's blimps, has been constructed entirely of timber. This enormous structure is 1,000 feet long, 153 feet high and has clearance span arches of 237 feet. The quantity of steel which would have been needed to build this in the ordinary way was 2,050 tons. The War Production Board in the United States has commented on the growth of this category of construction in glowing terms and referred to the "timber connector" system which enables timber to be used by strengthening the joints. Timber has not failed because of its lesser strength, but usually in the past it has been replaced because of the difficulty of providing really effective jointing of the wooden members. This problem is met and solved by the connector and has meant yet another of the non-violent, vital revolutions that have been produced by war-time needs, the effects of which will be felt for many a year after the war ends.

The report of the War Production Board referred to above is worth putting on record. It says:—

> "The steel-ringed timber connector, which is used to increase the strength of joints in wood construction, saved more than 400,000 tons of steel for essential war production in 1942.
>
> "Towers, bridges, hangars, warehouses and numerous other Government wartime construction requirements have been built of wood reinforced with timber connectors.
>
> "The highest wood tower that could be built before the development of this improved technique was limited to eighty feet. Height was restricted because of the weakness of supporting joints. With the strength-utilizing property of the timber connector, wood towers, meeting all engineering requirements and specifications, may reach a height of 300 feet.
>
> "Approximately 200,000 tons of structural steel have been saved by the use of timber in a single military construction programme."

The modern timber connector had a rather interesting origin. Various types of connectors have for many years been used in some European countries; but the development of most of the efficient modern types was the work of a timber trade association of the United States— the National Lumber Manufacturers Association. They spent nearly £100,000 on the research which led up to their discovery and development, and some thirty American University colleges conducted their own experiments in these new methods of timber construction. It provides an outstanding example of a trade association initiating research

to aid the consumption of the product in which it is interested, and at
once conferring benefit not only upon the trade itself but bringing to
the community at large a valuable invention.

An American constructional engineer has given the following de-
scription of the working of the important split-ring type of connector;
it is interesting enough for the future to give his explanation in full:—

> "Timber connector split rings are split across at one point, the split being
> in the form of a tongue and slot. The purpose of the tongue-and-slot split is
> to provide for adjustment of the joint under service conditions. The split
> ring operates as follows; To insert a timber connector between two pieces of
> timber to form a joint, each facing piece first is grooved to receive the ring.
> One half of the ring is inserted in the groove of one of the two timber members
> and the other half into the groove of the other member, so that, when the
> two members are joined face to face, the ring is wholly imbedded between
> them. The circular grooves, each one-half the depth of the ring, are cut with
> a special grooving tool to a dimension slightly larger than the unexpanded
> circumference of the ring which is to be inserted. When the ring is forced
> into the groove, the tongue-and-slot split is forced apart slightly. When the
> ring is thus imbedded in the timber with its split slightly parted, it can expand
> or contract with the wood and thus form at all times a tight and rigid connection.
> The connecting through bolt is relieved of stress by the imbedded connector
> ring, and serves principally to hold the two timber members together, face
> to face. In the past, weakness at the bolted connections had retarded the
> use of timber as heavy structural material. Pound for pound, timber has the
> strength of steel, but its bolted joints were its Achilles heel. The timber
> connector spreads the load on a timber joint over practically the entire cross
> section of the wood and thus brings into play the full structural strength of
> the lumber. Other types of connectors, having teeth, are forced into the
> wood, no pre-grooving being necessary."

The saving in steel is enormous since one pound of steel in the
form of connectors saves about $13\frac{1}{2}$ times as much structural steel. In
the largest timber-built factory in the world, the Douglas assembly
plant in the United States, thirty thousand tons of steel were saved by
the use of timber joined together with the connector. Not only in factory
and general building work but also in bridge construction these new
methods are becoming more and more popular, and the U.S. Public
Roads Administration have used several 160 feet through-trusses for
the Alaska Highway. It was found that this assembly, which was a
combination of the timber connector and glued laminations, showed a
considerable saving both in cost and time of erection. There seems little
doubt that the engineers of the future will be able to build still further
on these new foundations and bring to the science of construction novel
and startling production methods.

Great strides have been made in the science of gluing joints, and in
the United States a wooden hangar has been built with thirteen glued-up
arches to house one of the projected Douglas DC-4 air monsters, which
will have a wing span of 117 feet and a length of nearly 93 feet. For
this particular building, three tons of glue were used to hold together
some 52,000 lineal feet of timber and, incidentally, the glue itself was
manufactured from wood in the first instance. At first the gluing of
structural members presented some perplexing problems such as the
difficulty of obtaining a high temperature glue line when the members

were anything up to twelve inches square; or the problem of ensuring that the natural seasoning of the wood after it had been erected did not weaken the joint. The methods now employed entail treating the members first with a hot solution of preservative which removes the surface sap from the cells and limits the amount of seasoning distortion. The members to be glued are then coated with the chosen adhesive, clamped together with a pressure of up to 200 pounds to the square inch and the whole set, complete with clamps, immersed in boiling water for the period necessary to complete the bonding. In the case of warm temperature setting synthetic resin glues, this period varies from half an hour for a four inch square beam to six hours for a twelve inch square.

In this country only limited use has been made of timber to replace structural steel in a similar way, mainly because of the difficulty of obtaining the large sizes and the enormous quantity of heavy timbers that would be required for such work. Some buildings, however, have been so constructed but since all the timber has to be imported the saving is not so manifest. In the case of Canada and the United States, ordnance factories, aircraft plants and hangars, army centres and bases are but a few of the erections where the trees of the forest have made a supreme contribution to the Allied war effort.

Timber connectors and new glue methods are bringing to timber fresh fame as a constructional material; one further development is adding to the potential value of wood for building—scientific stress grading. Timber has for many centuries acted as the main material of construction, and was so used long before engineers, mathematicians or scientists had worked out and made known their findings on the subject of mechanical properties. Some say that timber buildings have been erected for ten thousand years without anyone having the slightest idea of the exact relationship between the size and quality of the timber used and the "load" it had to carry. The theories on mechanical properties which were first enunciated in a very simple form by Robert Hooke in 1678, have been widely developed and applied to every constructional material with the exception of timber. Timbermen have never tried to grade their product to meet engineering standards but have, until recently, fallen back upon the threadbare argument that as "timber grows", it must be accepted for better or worse. Today, under the impetus of war, a change is taking place. Those capable of a scientific approach to timber problems maintain that owing to this ignorance of mechanical properties, timber which has to undergo stress tends to be used in sizes much bigger than are really necessary to take the load with safety. As a result, timber appears to be unduly expensive by comparison with other material because lack of stress grades forces the architect or engineer to over-estimate his safety factor to allow for knots, shakes and other defects or the unknown behaviour of the timber. In the future it is hoped that definite standard specifications will be evolved which will enable the user to consult a table and decide upon a certain stress grade as adequate for his particular job. The house-builder, for example, will know the load to be carried by his floor joists; from his tables he will be able to determine what grade and timber he should use. Such specifications will probably mean revolutionary changes in the grading methods of the mills in exporting countries, but unless timber producers realise that they live in a scientific age, many opportunities will be lost to exploit the full potentialities of an old and tried servant of man.

*　　*　　*　　*　　*　　*

When Germany was fast preparing for this gigantic onslaught and also in the early days of the war, much was heard of her making food, boots, clothes and a hundred and one other articles from wood. The stories told were always repeated in a half-humorous tone, as if this was the sign of some particularly decadent kind of economy. It was another example of folly, to add to the cardboard tanks and the fall of Hitler that was coming every day since the blood bath of June, 1934. It was in fact no sign of decadence: on the contrary, it suggested the existence of a chemical industry leaping ahead of the democratic countries, as it had done before, and pressing into the service of the war machine all its vast accumulated knowledge to provide the German army with many of the things it needed from the forest resources on the spot. The German forests are considerable, exceeding 30 million acres in extent, and they contain many thousands of cubic feet of excellent timber, particularly softwoods. More than one-and-a-half million workers were employed in all branches of the industry including wood distillation, and Germany led the world in employing her timber supplies to make chemicals, alcohol, industrial products, the range of which will never be fully known until the end of the war. While the democracies were using vast tonnages of timber on wood pulp for paper, the Germans were pulping their timber to produce the wide variety of products which lie within the trunk of every tree. It is possible that by their "autarkie" they paid a very high economic price for all the chemicals and products that they made, but they built up a system which was capable of producing many of the materials and explosives which they knew the Allied blockade would deny them when war came. They were preparing for just such a war; and when their first conquests brought them into the middle of the well stocked forest areas of Poland and Czechoslovakia —not to mention Austria—they were provided with all the raw material they required for many months ahead.

At long last, there are signs that on the Allied side, too, new products are being manufactured from the chemical constituents of the trees that grow. Some of these have been known for many years and attempts have been made to use them; but in general the ability of scientists to break down wood substance to yield many of the raw materials needed by an industrial system has been hindered as much by insufficient eagerness on the part of industry to supply the money for the research required as by the cheapness of substitutes. Yet in the growing tree, behind that drab-looking bark, there lies a whole host of valuable products waiting to be isolated and extracted.

The chemical structure of wood has been understood by scientists for many years, but the mysteries of some of its constituents are still being probed. Like all living matter, the tree itself is made up of numerous cells joined together which when alive contain some water and small quantities of other substances. The cell walls are the wood matter and the heavier hardwoods, for example, usually have very thick walls with small cell cavities. It is this fibrous substance of the cell walls which is of interest to the industrial chemist, since although the cavities themselves may contain quantities of minerals, oils, resins, tannins, gums and salts, the amounts are small and not normally of commercial interest as extractives. The infiltrates do, however, affect the uses to which some woods can be put since their presence may render the timber useless for woodpulp; or in the case of the tannin in oak, make it unsuitable for general employment in contact with ferrous metals. The substance of these cell walls is made up of cellulose, hemicelluloses and lignin, and these three together give to the wood the same rough percentages of carbon (50 per cent.), oxygen (44 per cent.), and hydrogen (6 per cent.) irrespective of the species tested.

Cellulose is one of the most interesting and promising discoveries in the field of industrial processes which the last fifty years has produced. The substance accounts for more than 50 per cent. of the solid tissue of wood and is merely carbon, hydrogen and oxygen combined in certain proportions. There is nothing very mysterious about this combination, and in fact sugar and starch are of exactly the same constituents but combined in a different ratio. Man can digest a certain amount of starch but he cannot digest cellulose—if he could, it would have opened up unexpected and unlimited possibilities in the use of wood matter as human food. The purest form is found in cotton and flax fibres, and the fact that in wood matter cellulose is combined with other substances which have to be dissolved in order to obtain a pure extract limited its use in pre-war days. It is colourless and insoluble in solvents such as water and alcohol and in general resistant to chemical action. It is, however, highly soluble in a limited number of acids such as hydrochloric and sulphuric acids provided the concentration is sufficiently strong. Cellulose is the most important of the natural polysaccharides and its molecular construction (glucose-anhydride units) has a significant bearing upon its use as the basis of numerous plastic materials. In the last ten years it has been the subject of major developments and now figures as the foundation of a whole variety of industrial and consumers products from artificial silk to celluloid, from paper to explosives.

Cellulose is found in the fibres, and the substance acting as a "binder" to keep these fibres together is lignin, which constitutes about

25 per cent. of the total wood matter. Less is known of the possibilities of lignin or of its chemical constituents, although it is believed to contain more carbon and less oxygen than cellulose, and is found in the wood combined in differing proportions with cellulose depending upon the type of tree under examination. Some of the mysteries of lignin are approaching solution and chemists in the United States and Canada have isolated it, using it in the manufacture of various kinds of binders or substances such as glycols, glycerine, phenols for plastics, water softeners for locomotives and vanilla flavouring. A whole range of plastic materials has been produced with the help of lignin, and it would seem that it can be extracted from waste at a very low cost and should bulk large in the plastics chemistry of the post-war period. It can be separated from cellulose by a simple method which is the basis of the chemical processes used in the manufacture of wood-pulp. During the production of pulp and paper, large quantities of lignin emerge as waste products, and it is therefore of great interest to the industry to discover methods of turning this waste into useful by-products.

The hemicelluloses make up the remaining small percentage of the total wood matter and, although they too are polysaccharides, very little is known of their true nature except that they are more affected by dilute acids and alkalies than is cellulose proper.

Wood-pulp is the most important and best known product directly derived from trees and some mention of its part in the economic life of Canada has already been made. The paper which has become so important a part of the daily life of civilised communities is manufactured from this wood-pulp, but until comparatively recent times paper was made from cotton and linen rags. The first trace in history of paper manufacture was in China in A.D. 105, and then the materials were the bark of mulberry trees, bamboo bark and rope which were pounded together in water and dried in sheets. The Arabs learned the trade from the Chinese some 650 years afterwards, and the knowledge gradually spread from Arabia to North Africa until the Moors introduced it into Spain about 1150 A.D. The first English paper mill was founded by John Tate in 1494, and some two hundred years later the New World began to copy the methods of the Old with rags as the basis. Today an enormous industry has been built up upon the demand for reading and writing papers as well as wrappings of all kinds, and Canada, as the world's largest producer of pulp, has played a leading part in the development of paper making. At the present time the limitations placed upon the size of the daily paper are due not only to the fact that ships cannot be spared to bring the pulp and paper over here; the main reason is that both are urgently required for purposes more directly connected with the war effort. In fact wood-pulp has become one of the primary raw materials used in the manufacture of a large number of substances and articles vital to the efficient waging of war and, although home propaganda has very effectively acquainted the man in the street with the need for more and more paper for containers of all kinds, there is a great deal which cannot yet be said of the other derivatives of wood-pulp.

Canada installed the first pulping plant in 1860 and experience has shown her that spruce, hemlock and balsam are the most satisfactory woods to use. There are three separate stages in the production of paper—pulpwood, wood-pulp and paper itself. The first is the name given to the raw timber prepared in the forests for the pulping plants, and, incidentally, most of the provinces in Canada have for some time past prohibited the export of pulp-wood—legislation which has undoubtedly served to put the industry upon a sound basis so that it now leads the world. The other main producers of pulp are the Soviet Union, Finland and Germany, although some of the pre-war European countries, such as Poland and Latvia, were beginning to develop an impressive industry which could not, however, have aspired to the proportions of the Canadian industry in view of the smaller quantity of raw material available in those countries.

The pulp-wood is manufactured into wood-pulp by any one of four different methods and in general it depends upon the type of paper required which method is employed. The first is called the "mechanical" method and produces what is known as "groundwood" pulp. As its name implies, this process consists of grinding the wood against a grindstone which breaks down and so separates the fibres; the resulting groundwood is then washed, screened and prepared for paper making. For ordinary newsprint, cheap wall papers, packings, containers of all kinds and coarse boards, this is the best and cheapest method to employ. The three other processes are all of a chemical nature and derive their names from the different types of chemical used as the means of dissolving away the non-cellulose components of the wood material, leaving pure cellulose in the form of a pulp. The cellulose itself is practically unaffected by the chemicals used—and in fact by the majority of chemicals—so that the resulting pulp produces paper of the highest quality which will endure without deterioration for a great length of time. It is an interesting fact that bacteria and fungi do not thrive on cellulose and thus paper which is made from pure cellulose will have great durability under normal conditions of use or storage. The groundwood pulp naturally contains other substances in addition to cellulose, so that with the purer pulps it is possible to produce papers of greater durability, strength and of superior appearance.

The three chemical processes for the manufacture of pulp are the sulphite, the soda and the sulphate or kraft processes and each of these is extensively used in normal times. With the sulphite process, the wood is cleaned and chipped into small particles about an inch long, crushed under pressure and cooked by steam in big "digesters" with acid bisulphite liquor. It is used either by itself or mixed with lower quality pulps to make various kinds of paper, and in the bleached form it is the main raw pulp for artificial silk production. The soda process is usually employed to break down the wood from the lighter hardwood trees such as poplar, and because the fibres produced are weak the papers made by this process are lacking in strength although they have an excellent surface. The sulphate process was designed to reduce the cost of the more expensive soda method by the use of salt cake instead of soda ash. The result is a paper of great strength and flexibility which is mainly employed for kraft paper, miscellaneous wrappings and bags. The chemicals used are very similar to the soda process, for in the one case sodium carbonate (soda ash) is used and in the other sodium sulphate (salt cake).

The actual production of paper is a secondary product of wood—that is from the pulp described above—but there are several interesting features about the paper-maker's art which are worth detailing. The principle of paper construction is that the fibres of the cellulose wood pulp stick to each other very strongly when the water dries away and that, surprisingly enough, this adhesive quality is only induced by water and by no other liquids. The length and width of the wood fibres in the cellulose govern the strength and surface of the papers produced from the pulp. The natural fibres can be spread out when wet by beating, and the paper-maker's skill is marked by the manner in which he can "beat" his pulp to obtain the required strength and surface. The machine employed to make tissue is specially designed to feed the thin material to the rollers without it disintegrating in the process. The sheet is formed upon the wire screen, as in the case of other papers, but since it is not strong enough to travel from the screen to the press a wool blanket meets the sheet as soon as it leaves the screen and supports it into the press, the action of which is to "mangle" out the majority of the moisture.

Some of the main products made from cellulose, other than paper, have already been mentioned and an exhaustive list would run into many pages. Synthetic cellulose textiles are the most important group, and they comprise the articles variously referred to as artificial silk and rayon. The greater proportion of these textiles is made from bleached sulphite pulp by the viscose process, which consists of submitting the cellulose to a chemical process and a treacley, coagulated substance, viscose, emerges. If this is then treated with acid, it can be drawn out into fine threads which when made into yarns, washed and dyed, can be woven into elegant and hardy materials. Viscose processing is not the only method of producing artificial silk, and from time to time new inventions have added to the knowledge of the subject and helped to reduce the cost of production. Cellophane is a variety of the substance and is useful for many purposes since it is air-proof and can be rendered moisture-proof by coating with nitro-cellulose.

Other important by-products of cellulose are artificial leather, gramophone records, vulcanised fibres, sausage skins, aeroplane wings, paints and varnishes—a list which gives some idea of the almost unlimited

moving the plywood half shell of a Mosquito fuselage from the jig.

Photo: M.O.I.

oto: *U.S. Forest Service.*

The Giant Curtiss C-76, the first U.S. transport plane to be built almost entirely of wood.

The British Horsa Glider, constructed largely
of plywood and timber.

Photo: Admiralty.

Photo: M.O.I.

Merchant ship under construction in British
yards. A vast quantity of timber uprights and
stage deals surround it.

small, fast naval combat craft built mainly from timber.

Photo: Admiralty (Keystone).

Photo: Admiralty.

An assault landing craft of timber construction —oak keel and mahogany skins.

R.A.F. fast Air-Sea Rescue launch—another timber-built boat.

Photo: M.O.I.

Photo: M.O.I.

150 feet bridge erected by R.E.s. A high proportion of the structure is timber.

Constructing a timber trestle-type bridge, Washington, U.S.A.

Photo: U.S. Forest Service.

Photo: M.O.I.

Miners at the coal face. Timber props and crowns support the roof.

**Temporary timber buildings under construction
in Washington, U.S.A.**

Photo: U.S. Forest Serv.

**Aircraft factory under construction in Kansas,
U.S.A., built with the use of timber connectors.**

Photo: U.S. Forest Serv.

Photo: Army Air Corps, U.S.

**Bomber Hangar with 152 feet beam arch
built from one inch laminated timber.**

...ge School in Karelia, U.S.S.R., constructed from local timber.

Photo: Society for Cultural Relations with the U.S.S.R.

...o: U.S. Forest Service.

Rotary veneer cutting machine.

100 feet wood tower in the Clark National Forest, Missouri, U.S.A.

4

variety of industrial products that cellulose and viscose can provide. The part that these substances will play in the future of plastics cannot yet be foreseen; yet it is certain that through the pulping of wood matter and the extraction of cellulose vast new possibilities lie before industry in its search for plentiful and cheap materials to replace those the supply of which is receding as the years go by.

*   *   *   *   *   *

What is usually known as the destructive distillation of wood provides the second main group of chemical processes, and it is entirely different from the production of cellulose and its ancillary products. Wood distillation breaks down the chemical elements of the tree trunk and yields many things of industrial value. The full process gives first charcoal, then tar, some miscellaneous acids, and finally acetate of lime and crude wood alcohol. The acetate of lime can be reconverted into acetic acid or acetone, both of which have medicinal and industrial uses. Publicity has been given to the few unscrupulous persons who took advantage of the shortage of genuine alcohol during war time to foist upon the public what became known as "hooch", which was usually wood alcohol. Wood chips are placed in a retort or oven and heated without the addition of any moisture, in other words "distilled", and gases are given off which pass through a condenser. In normal times, wood alcohol was used in the production of such things as aniline dyes and explosives. It is wise to mention that this alcohol gives off fumes which are dangerous to inhale, and it is perhaps unnecessary to add that the drinking of even small quantities of the liquid can lead to blindness or may even be fatal.

In spite of the large number of products which can be derived from wood by distillation, it is unwise to overstress the importance of these processes, since many of the products can be more easily obtained from other substances. A number of derivatives are impure, such as methyl alcohol, which is only used as a cheap solvent by the chemical industry, and the extension of distillation will depend upon the cost of the competing materials.

A different yet perhaps more promising branch of chemical extraction from wood is the production of ethyl alcohol from wood waste. It is believed that the Germans have been extensively engaged upon this ever since war began and have succeeded in meeting many of their demands for industrial alcohols, which are required in the making of synthetic rubbers—to mention but one of their numerous uses. During the last war, they used a hydrolysis process to extract wood sugar from waste, and from this sugar they made alcohol by fermentation. Between the wars a German, Scholler, greatly improved the method of production and now the United States have several test plants in operation. Most of the engineers responsible for the developments in America were refugees from Hitler's Germany, and they brought with them knowledge which has been of immense value to the Allies' war effort. The importance of these processes is not limited to war conditions, for such strides have been made as will make production economical even in peace time.

Every mill piles up enormous heaps of waste of all kinds—sawdust, chips, offcuts and the rest—and these should be made the raw material of alcohol production. Normally the demand is met mainly from molasses and grain, but it is likely that for some years after the war both of these products will be in limited supply. Experiments carried out by the U.S. Office of Production Research and Development at a plant in Michigan gave results which confirm the view that at least fifty gallons of alcohol can be obtained from one ton of dry waste and at costs which compare favourably with molasses, grain or ethylene gas emerging during the process of cracking petroleum. The main waste which is left over from the hydrolysis process is lignin and if sufficient uses can be found for this by-product in the chemical and plastics industries, it will reduce still further the costs of producing wood sugar. Since the war consumption of the United States is in the region of seven hundred million gallons of industrial alcohol, these are developments of great significance.

In the United States, experiments in the production of a suitable food for cattle have been made with sawdust and wood. At the Dairy Department of the University of Wisconsin some years ago a food was manufactured from sawdust which when mixed with a condensed sugar solution extracted from the sawdust in the first process, proved as successful as ordinary meal. In this particular case the synthetic meal was combined with the ordinary food in the proportions of one-third to two-thirds. Many rumours have been heard that the Germans, in their desire to produce greater quantities of food for their harassed peoples, have tried to make various kinds of food for human consumption from sawdust, and it is quite possible that they have succeeded to a limited extent. The difficulty is to make the meal digestible, and until this chemical obstacle has been overcome, the possibility of extensive development in this sphere is limited.

There are still a number of other products from wood or wood waste which merit mention as although some of them are in common use, there are opportunities for development, and probably something has already been done to extend the scope of their usefulness. A novel and promising variation is the manufacture of a wool substitute from the bark of the American redwood tree. The U.S. War Production Board has received a report from its Research Division on this experiment, which claims to be able to obtain about 120 million pounds of synthetic wool from bark waste. This is not a great quantity and is about one-tenth of the total that is required to fit up an army of four million men; but in war time it may be a necessary step to take to relieve shortages. The general idea is to mix the "bark wool" with standard fibres to produce a wool product which is in some respects superior to ordinary

natural wool since it is a better insulator and more resistant to fire and
rot. Another use which has become familiar to many is the sawdust
producer gas unit, which is fitted to the rear of an ordinary motor-car
or lorry. Two hundred pounds of any kind of sawdust will take the car
some seventy-five to one hundred miles, and the whole apparatus weighs
less than half a ton. The Germans have not been idle in developing this
method of substituting producer gas for petrol and the Stockholm
Correspondent of *The Times*, writing in January, 1944, said:—

> "Various raw fuels are being used in central and western Germany, but
> the whole of the transport for the Russian front is being adapted for generators
> using wood and charcoal. To supply this the Germans have created an
> elaborate system of factories to produce 'tankwood' ('tank' in German usage
> has only its original meaning, and not that of a fighting-machine), as only
> specially prepared wood-blocks can be used for this purpose.
> "They fell trees and transport them to the sawmills where they are sawn
> and chopped into suitable small blocks and artificially dried in special ovens;
> a certain proportion are converted into charcoal as the generators will not
> work without a foundation of charcoal. This process yields also the by-product
> of tar, from which the factories extract oil. The oil is regarded as especially
> valuable and is sent to Germany for industry.

What are known as "naval stores" are also products from wood;
these are mainly turpentine, resin and pitch and are sometimes obtained
from the living tree by "orcharding", or from the stumps of trees already
felled where such trees have a high resin content. Charcoal was one of
the earliest, and in the past the most important products from wood
although its main use—in the manufacture of iron—has been superseded
by cheaper and more efficient processes. In the present war it has been
widely consumed industrially and not its least important use was for
the filters of gas-masks, since if properly treated it has high gas-absorbing
powers. The tough qualities of "glass" which go to make up the tank
windscreen or the windshield in a plane have as a basis a kind of celluloid
from wood cellulose, although they belong properly to the plastics
class of products from wood. Some types of glass made in this manner
are very weather resistant and can take pressures up to 15,000 lbs. to
the square inch, which is greatly in excess of the resistance of ordinary
glass. They work with ease and can be bent and cut as required; the
thicker material—one inch or more—is used as bullet and splinter protection for a wide variety of war purposes.

*   *   *   *   *   *

So much is heard today of the important part that will be played in
the future by the plastic aeroplane, motor-car, wireless cabinet, sewing
machine, refrigerator and armchair that many may wonder whether
this new plastic age will really dawn. Undoubtedly, there have been
very great developments in the production and use of plastic materials,
but even before the war a not inconsiderable proportion of the articles
of everyday life were made in some plastic form. The interesting point
is that the limit to the development in this direction has by no means
been reached, and war-time experience will have contributed many

new features to the science. Much of the general theory of plastics has been the possession of scientists and industrialists for a number of years, but the problem has been to produce at a cost which compared favourably with the raw materials already in use. Now there are signs that this will be possible, and it is not unreasonable to expect the production of a whole range of consumers' goods in plastics.

Plastics can be divided into three distinct categories of products. There are first of all those belonging to a group which are at base plywood, manufactured directly from timber, and in order to get an idea of what these are, something will have to be said on the general question of plywood. Secondly, there is a group technically known as "thermo-setting plastics", and the most prominent of these is the trade product "Bakelite". Thirdly, a group called "thermo-plastics", one of which has already been mentioned above in dealing with the synthetic glasses used in tanks and aircraft.

Modern times have seen very great advances in the development of plywood manufacture, but the basic idea is not a new one. In the New York Metropolitan Museum of Art there is an Egyptian casket made from plywood which is about four thousand years old. In those days, its value was largely derived from the decorative qualities veneering could endow to a piece of furniture or an ornament; today the use has spread to almost every branch of industry. The cutting of thin "slices" of wood—known as veneers—has already been described, and it is these veneers glued together that make up a piece of plywood. Usually, the great strength of plywood is due to the building up of the sheet of wood with the grain of each veneer at right angles to its neighbours, so that the natural tendency of each layer to split along the grain or swell under the influence of moisture is resisted by the adjacent layer where the grain of the wood runs in the opposite direction. The most difficult part of the whole process was the sticking together of the sheets to make up the thicker board, for the glues in general use in the early days of this century were not sufficiently strong to resist moisture or heavy wear and tear, so that in time the plies would begin to come asunder. The early glues were usually vegetable in composition and not only did they fail to withstand the effects of moisture, but they were very pleasant food for all kinds of low forms of life which would feed on them, weakening and eventually destroying the boards.

The three types of glues are the animal, vegetable and synthetic resins which are sometimes described as waterproof, non-waterproof and water-resistant. The advantages of glues such as those made from casein or soya beans is that, although they are less resistant than the synthetic resins, their ease of application encourages their use. These glues can be mixed with ordinary tap water, and the dissolving of the glue powder is a physical action which will take place with normal temperatures but which is made more rapid if heat is applied. The synthetic resin glues may be used in either hot or cold presses but the best results are obtained with the former. The two types most favoured today are urea-formaldehyde and phenol-formaldehyde. The important thing about these glues is that they are extremely strong and are highly resistant to the effects of moisture: this is not to say that if a piece of plywood so glued were to be immersed in water for a number of years it would emerge unscathed. It probably would not, but for ordinary purposes, such as the all-weather surfaces of aircraft or in small boats where spray and water can be expected to wash over, this type of plywood is extremely effective and durable. It is almost impossible to strip off the plies that have been glued up by this process (the glue line often being stronger than the wood itself), and the general strength properties of synthetic resin glues enable plywoods made from them to be used wherever hard wear is demanded.

The most skilful part of all plywood manufacture, especially when using the new types of glues, is the operation of the press to ensure that pressure, heat and the moisture content of the veneers are all correct. Mistakes on these points, or irregularly cut veneers can render the final plywood sheet useless for work such as aircraft where the manufacture must be mathematically accurate.

The most important developments in gluing processes were being made by the Germans before this war and some of the present British methods are based upon German patents. Now the Americans and Canadians, under the stimulus of war, are going forward rapidly in this field. One kind of synthetic resin glue is manufactured in big thin sheets which are laid between the plies or veneers and the pressure applied under heat to mould the whole series of layers into a solid piece of plywood. The application of the heat has presented several problems, and experiments are now being carried out in the use of electric currents to do this work. The advantage of such a method is that the "glue line" in the assembly of layers attains a higher temperature than the surrounding wood—just what is required to provide correct bonding. Before the war a German firm used a novel method of combining big timber assemblies. Thin wire gauze was coated with glue and placed between the timber or plies which were to be joined together. Through this gauze was passed a low voltage current which heated the glue and rapidly bonded the wooden plies together, giving a strong finish and very rapid production. There must be many possibilities for the extension of this principle of electrically induced heat for the binding of veneer with resin glues.

A development of gluing which has spread over into the field of plastics proper, is the use of synthetic urea resin and several associated products for "moulding" wood. Urea is a common ammonia salt, and has the valuable effect upon wood of making it pliable so that it can be moulded into any shape required and, on cooling it will set hard and remain in the moulded form. A recent discovery in Canada has been called a "wood-alloy", and the inventor took wood and treated it with

PLYWOOD IMPORTS INTO U.K. IN 1937

Country	Percentage
Finland	36·53
Russia	24·25
Latvia	7·68
Poland	6·12
Japan	5·96
U.S.A.	3·45
Canada	3·34
Germany	2·63
Estonia	2·13
Lithuania	1·79
Sweden	1·64
France	0·76
Rumania	0·65
Czecho-slovakia	0·55
Other sources	2·52

PERCENTAGE OF TOTAL IMPORTS

The percentages are based upon cubic quantities. In 1937 the total volume of imports was just under 16 million cubic feet.

urea-formaldehyde, heated it to the temperature of boiling water and found that the wood became completely plastic and could be formed to any shape while warm and set firm when it cooled off. There have been many developments in this type of compressed wood, and one process of treating plywood with raw resin produced a dense hard dark brown substance something like marble in appearance which has been a success in the manufacture of propellers. Similar experiments have been carried out with paper in place of plywood. Numbers of paper sheets were subjected to a pressure of 200-300 lbs. to the square inch, and the resulting board was almost equal in strength to steel of the same dimensions, but half the weight of aluminium.

There have recently been made public details of similar types of impregnated wood with names such as "compreg", "impreg", "homogenised" wood and many others. One of the most recent was that patented by the American chemical firm of Du Pont De Nemours and given the name of "transmuted wood". The process consists of impregnating the wood with a solution of uncondensed methylolurea; after drying the wood is heated to 240 degrees F. or more so that the resin fuses, fills the cell cavities and, when cool, sets hard. The resulting material is strong, with the appearance of timber, but resistant to water, alcohol and mild concentrations of acid; it is also said to be very durable. It is possible to foresee considerable developments in the use of "resinised" woods of this type if production costs can be made sufficiently low.

These are all in the "near-plastics" group and are obviously the most important to producers and users of timber. A few words must be said on the other two groups which are plastics proper and whose detailed treatment therefore is the job of the plastics engineer. The thermosetting plastics undergo chemical change when subjected to heat and pressure; after this change no added heat or pressure will alter their form. A mixture of formalin, carbolic acid and ammonia is gently heated and when cool produces a hard brittle resinous substance. This is powdered up and mixed with sawdust or wood flour in the proportions of one of resin to six of sawdust, churned up together and gently warmed. The synthetic material which emerges is cooled, then powdered, and it is this powder which when heated and moulded under pressure can be formed into any shape required and will retain that shape indefinitely. The thermoplastic materials, such as the vulcanite already mentioned, can be softened under pressure and heat at any time, provided that such application is not sufficient to cause chemical decomposition. All the cellulose plastics are included in this group, whilst the phenolic and casein plastics are in the thermosetting group.

The full value of plastics to modern industry has not yet been tested, and there are many who are sceptical of the place that this new science will play in the future. Others believe that the cost of production will always place them outside the main demand of the mass-production industry, but there are, however, so many manifest advantages that they enjoy over other materials that their adoption for numerous industrial purposes is assured. Already such materials are largely used in electrical appliances since they can be moulded and are non-conductors. Their other virtues are that they are very strong and light (although more brittle than timber and so unlikely to replace it for building work), can withstand wide ranges of temperatures without decomposition and are highly acid-resistant. They are constantly being employed to replace for certain uses materials such as wood, aluminium and tungsten, and for many purposes they have qualities superior to natural resin products, rubber and similar substances. Their application to wood yields a moulded product which is often lighter than ordinary solid wood for the same strength ratio.

The foregoing is but a brief outline of the main chemical and non-chemical products that are to be found in the living tree and the many war time uses to which timber has been put. There is still much to be said of the place of timber in the war economy, but most of this cannot be told until the end of hostilities makes a full disclosure possible. The facts as at present available do, however, make one thing appear certain —there is very little visible limit to the possibilities of timber usage; and although the present methods of employing wood as a direct product cut from the tree may have to be revised to meet the requirements of a more specialised industrial system, the physical demand for wood of all kinds is not likely to decrease but rather, with the wise development of the latent possibilities, will continue to increase as it has done ever since the first shipload was brought to this country 150 years ago. There will always be a certain need for timber in its natural form of logs and planks, but in addition further changes can be expected such as the employment of heavy timber in the larger types of building, made possible by inventions similar to the timber connector. Secondly, plywoods and plastics are but on the threshold of development as servants of an advanced industrial community; and lastly, the chemical treatment of wood material in order to wring from its nature chemicals, fabrics, papers, and a thousand other materials is as yet in its infancy, and in a few decades new possibilities will have emerged which at the moment are still in the experimental stage. These are the portents of the future and the wise industrialist and scientist should be able to collaborate to produce a novel range of derivatives of wood to ease man's burden and beautify his existence and surroundings. War will thus have done something by unleashing new possibilities to make amends for the destruction it has wrought.

"I know it is an objection, or rather an unreasonable excuse of the slothful neglect of successive and continual planting, upon so tedious an expectation of what is not likely to be timber in our time: But as this is quite otherwise (provided men would be early at the work) they might have sufficient of their own planting (nay, from the very rudiment and seeds) abundantly to recompense their patience and attendance, living to the age men usually attain, by the common course of nature; with how much more improvement to their children and posterity? and this minds me of what's reported of the Emperor Maximilian the IId. That by chance finding an ancient husbandman setting date-stones, asks him what his meaning was to plant a tree that required an hundred years before it bare any fruit? Sir, replies the good man, I have children, and they may have more come after them."

JOHN EVELYN: *Sylva*

CHAPTER IV

TREES FOR THE FUTURE

THE PROBLEM of planning the after-war world will call for an effort as immense as that needed to win the war itself. It will not just be a matter of getting discharged soldiers back into jobs again; something more will be demanded this time, and every one of the nation's natural resources must be brought into the plan to better the standard of life. No one should remain outside and no one should be permitted to encourage sectional interests at the expense of those of the community as a whole.

Where can the trees of the countryside come into the picture of this new world? Will they in fact have any place in Britain's economic future: if so, how will their production and conversion be organised? Is it to be a State matter, as in so many other countries, or, if not, who will do this important work? To be able to answer such questions presupposes some knowledge of the kind of society to be created in the next decade, for in the case of forestry there are economic and social aspects to be considered.

There will be important changes within the timber industry itself. It is possible, for example, to envisage certain industries dispensing with the use of timber altogether as the result of new developments and inventions stimulated by the needs of war. It may, on the other hand, be considered that for some purposes the production of materials from timber rather than the timber itself provides the most economical method of employing resources. A strong possibility is that Britain may decide, in order to remain an exporter to the world's markets, that she cannot afford the "luxury" of sheltering a timber-growing industry on this island, which by increasing costs of production would place her at a disadvantage in the world's markets for manufactured products. Since Britain is small and will always find it difficult to compete with the countries of continental extent, such as Russia and North America, in the provision of large quantities of timber, the post-war problem for the industry will depend largely upon the kind of economic organisation decided upon and the place that Britain is to have in the world economy. It will not, of course, be dominated entirely by economic considerations, which are matters such as the price of imported timber compared with the price of the native product; or the relative importance of agriculture and forestry in the general scheme of things, for with a small country, after a certain point the land transferred to forestry will be at the expense of agriculture. Other important considerations will enter into the final decisions—whether for example it is socially desirable to have a small or moderate forestry industry, even though from the business point of view it does not "pay". There are numerous persons who deplore the drift away from the rural occupations and who now believe that with proper town and village planning many workers will be only too ready to go back to the quieter, more simple and, in many ways, happier life of the rural areas.

Thus everything will depend upon the shape of things in the post-war era as to the place such economic institutions as forestry and agriculture are to have. In the case of forestry, however, it is possible to go a little farther and give some of the facts which will have to be faced by any Government or reconstruction authority charged with planning for the future. These five facts are, as far as can be seen, non-controversial and provide a starting point:—

    i. Britain's great industrial demand for timber and the limited size of the country mean that some quantity of imported material will always be needed.

    ii. Many of Britain's Allies in this war—such as the Soviet Union, Canada, America, Norway, Yugoslavia, Poland—are important timber exporters and in course of time will re-enter the world's markets. It is not unreasonable to assume that they will look to the world's biggest timber importer and their former Ally as a suitable market.

    iii. Two major wars have now denuded Britain's forest lands and little replanting has been achieved. Positive action will be required to repair the damage and make a repetition of these two war timber crises less probable.

    iv. An extensive organisation existed in pre-war days for the handling of imported timber by docks, harbours, shipping companies, timber merchants and distributors. They will be seriously disturbed by—and probably resist—any radical change in the methods of meeting Britain's timber requirements.

    v. Trees do not reach full maturity for sixty to eighty years, so that any steps taken after this war will not be effective in meeting demand until the turn of the century. The possibility must be kept in mind that by that time changes may have taken place in industrial materials which render a proportion of the trees valueless from the economic viewpoint, although the investment may still be well worth while.

All these five points add up to the major dilemma—is it economically or socially desirable, or necessary because of some possible future war, to plant part of this small country with usable timber (which may not all be wanted by the time it is ready) and if so, what shall be the extent of this planting and what aid is demanded from the Government of the day?

The answer to such a question is naturally very complex and is still subject to many ifs and buts; but the report of the Forestry Commission on post-war forest policy did try in June, 1943, to suggest a plan for Britain for the next fifty odd years. An examination of its suggestions and the comments which followed the publication of the Report provide an answer to many of these questions. First of all, something must be said of the timber history of the last two hundred years.

*   *   *   *   *   *

The history of the forestry and timber industries of this country has never been written; if it had been, it would have very little to say until the nineteenth century on what was done to conserve resources or to encourage afforestation. The main demand came from the ship-builders, who needed quantities of native oaks for the fleets of men-o'-war. There were a few forests owned by the Crown and a number of individuals, such as John Evelyn, took a keen interest in forestry operations. Evelyn was one of the first exponents of scientific silviculture, and he wrote at a time when about one million oaks had been felled to build up the Navy of the Commonwealth. In his book, *Sylva*, he addressed himself to farmers and landowners, making an eloquent plea for the replanting of denuded areas so that British naval power, so dependent upon the native oaks, might be maintained and developed. It has been said that the Navy commanded with such historic effect by Nelson owes its existence to this Surrey squire, who combined the qualities of prophet and humanist and left his mark upon an age of profligacy. Writing towards the end of the seventeenth century in the days of the listless Charles the Second, when Spain's Empire with its worship of gold had begun to decline, he said: "We had better be without gold than without timber". At that time, England was going through one of its periods of timber famine when the demands of iron-smelting and glass making had made heavy calls upon the trees of the countryside.

Throughout the history of this country, wood was the main raw material until the new industrial methods of the nineteenth century ushered in the age of coal and iron. Most buildings were in wood and every so often grave shortages had been occasioned by the demands of some new invention or development, such as glass making or silver smelting, which consumed the trees of the forests at a rate that alarmed many, although few were moved to any useful action. The production of porcelain, the growth of the maritime fleets, the smelting of iron with charcoal, were responsible for the felling of countless trees all over the country. The city that burnt to ashes in the reign of Charles II was a wooden London and many rural buildings were constructed of timber right on until the last century. James Watt encased the first steam engine in wood, and many of the inventions of the Industrial Revolution were of wood construction, particularly those employed by the textile industry.

Despite the apparently obvious part that timber was playing in building up mercantile supremacy for Britain, little or nothing was done to conserve supplies, to find new sources, to develop silviculture, or to experiment on the species which were most suited to the climate and soil. But it would be unfair to apportion blame to the peoples and governments of those far off days until something has been heard of what was done one hundred and fifty, fifty or even ten years ago.

The first "Forestry Commission" was appointed in 1786 and was charged with the task of arranging for the planting of sufficient oaks to assure the nation's supplies for the British Navy. Plans were laid for the planting of 100,000 acres with oak trees; but the arrival of the iron ship not very long after made the work of the Commission, according to its terms of reference, unnecessary. A little foresight might have led the Government of the day, however harassed it was with other vital problems, to extend the powers and duties of the Commission, since the not very distant future was to prove that timber was required not only for the provision of men-o'-war but also for a thousand and one urgent industrial purposes throughout the nineteenth century.

In the succeeding years, an era of colonial expansion and maritime competition, a gradual development of imports of timber from across the seas was noticeable. First, the urgent needs of shipbuilding had led to the opening up of some of the vast virgin forests of the North American continent. Then, as traders sent their ships to the four corners of the earth, they brought back with them the exotic hardwoods of India, the mahoganies of Africa and the teak of the Indies. At first these woods were scarce and expensive; but the trade proved profitable and the volume grew until by the end of the century it was making fortunes for the few. The main softwood areas were not opened up until late in the century; for the first half of the hundred year period, Britain's annual imports did not exceed about fifty million cubic feet of all kinds of timbers. During the 'fifties, the vast areas of British Columbia and Canada generally began to be colonised and developed, so that before very long an export trade to this country was started. It was small at first and in the 'sixties amounted to only a fraction of Britain's total needs, but like a hardy plant, it flourished slowly and its roots were deep and sound. During the last twenty-five years of the century British yearly imports were in the neighbourhood of three hundred million cubic feet at a time when the wooden ship was practically forgotten, but industry had evolved many other profitable uses for the trees of the forests. All over the world, wherever the little trading ships called for cargoes and there were trees growing, the axe was at work and the saw was humming until the timber was flowing so readily into Britain's ports that at home fewer and fewer people showed any interest in the problem of native supplies. There was plenty of timber in other parts of the world, plenty of ships to bring it here, plenty of sailors to sail the ships—why worry about the meagre quantities in Britain that could only be wrested from an uncharitable Nature by hard work and at high cost?

It is understandable that during the nineteenth century those anxious to encourage forestry operations could find few sympathisers in high places. Imports were adequate to meet all demands, and there was no major war in which Britain was engaged to cut off her ships from the world routes or otherwise to exercise an unexpected drain upon her timber resources. A few warning voices were heard; but the effect of these eloquent pleas was negligible. Some brave, unsung, British silviculturists experimented with the introduction of new species and the so-called "exotic" conifers such as Douglas fir, Sitka spruce and Japanese larch were tried out and, when acclimatised, were found to be eminently suitable to the soil and climatic conditions of this country. In later years the experience of these unknown pioneers was of immense value in establishing forests which not only suit these islands but are of rapid growth and produce timber of excellent quality and supplement the indigenous Scots pine and the better known foreign stocks such as Norway spruce and European larch. Against the work of those who advanced silvicultural knowledge in this bleak period must be set the almost complete failure of the State to grapple with a problem which became daily more pressing, but it was not until the 1914 War that the real seriousness was fully realised—and by then it was too late.

The activities of the official Government agencies during the nineteenth century were very confined. The Office of Woods and Forests made a few moves in the right direction but their interest was limited. There were several other select Committees whose rulings did not in any way affect the main issue—had the Government of the day any clear-cut forestry policy capable of guaranteeing to the nation an adequate supply of timber in the years to come? At the turn of the century when the possibility of a major war with Imperial Germany began to loom large in the minds of those who were able to interpret events correctly, there was a slight increase in the interest in forestry operations. The Royal Commission on Coast Erosion and Forestry, sitting in 1909, produced an estimate that the total area which could be planted with trees in Great Britain was 8½ million acres. This can be compared with the total planted area today of something less than 3 million acres. This Commission did incidentally produce two schemes for re-planting which can be regarded as the forerunners of modern forestry plans. Nothing was done to implement the findings but the influence of this Commission was immediately felt, and certain allocations were made by the Treasury to assist forestry development.

Up to the beginning of the 1914 War there was, of course, no State Forestry and, with the exception of the few Crown Forests, all the woodlands were in private hands; and these private owners were certainly not doing very much to compensate for the lack of interest on the part of the Government. It is a sorry tale, for the majority of private woodlands during the period under review were badly planted, in a poor state of management and the usable timber available at the beginning of the last war was less than half of the total stand. The main defects during the nineteenth century can nearly all be attributed to two causes. First, no inducement was offered to the woodland owner to produce trees that the nation needed. Second, there was an unwillingness on the part of owners to acquaint themselves with up-to-date knowledge of silviculture; few were willing to call in the expert to solve the problems of their woodlands. They planted the wrong kinds of trees, they spaced them badly, they neglected the year-by-year treatment and care which is essential to give a good timber yield. In general, the planting was spasmodic with no eye upon the market that was available or the problems of the sawmill that had to cut the trees into commercially usable timber. Very little planting was done, and the new trees were the result of natural regeneration which, when uncontrolled, seldom produces the right trees in the right places. It is possible to have a piece of land ideally suited for the growing of one type of tree so overrun with pests such as rabbits and squirrels that no natural regeneration can be expected; another area may be quite unsuitable for correct growth and yet be free of such pests, so that trees of an inferior kind will take root and grow. The procedure of periodic thinning and felling was largely ignored, and there was a tendency to space the trees for artistic or ornamental motives, which usually means trees planted far apart, in order that they may develop low sweeping boughs. This kind of plantation produces knotty, ill-grown wood which no sawmiller wants and is a waste of the energies of the workers and of valuable tracts of land.

The results of this period can be seen from the report of the Forestry Commission in 1924, since the estates on which they were then commenting had been planted during the nineteenth century. The report states that some 16 per cent. of the total area had been felled and was in a very derelict condition, 11 per cent. was covered with useless scrub and 7 per cent. was for ornamental purposes only. The remaining areas were in general of very low quality and could not be expected to contribute a normal yield. Can it then be wondered that Britain enters major wars without sufficient timber and usually without enough ships to carry the vast quantities that she needs to prosecute a war?

Why did the landed proprietor of the nineteenth century fail so lamentably to guard his valuable possessions in the majority of cases? The reasons are manifold and are knit closely with the social and economic state of the country at varying periods in its history. An important economic factor which will have an overriding effect upon any new schemes is that an investment in forestry operations takes so many years to yield a return. This introduces a feature which is peculiar to the private owner—whether it is worth his while to look ahead eighty or one hundred years for the full enjoyment of an investment when, if he used his resources in some other project, he could see a return in his lifetime and the lifetime of his children. This provides the strongest argument for State interference in this particular branch of agriculture, for it is only the State, which is impersonal and therefore takes no count of time, that can afford to tie up its resources for a return so distant. The State can weigh carefully the issues that are involved both now and for the future when the forests mature, but the private individual is either unable or unwilling, especially if possessed only of fairly limited resources, to take such decisions.

In addition to this reluctance on the part of landowners to undertake long period planning, many of them were not very interested in the replanting of their woodlands. At some bad period in their financial history they were perhaps forced to sell a few hundred trees at a very cheap price; they rarely worried whether these felled trees were replaced, or if they did consider the matter, they were seldom capable of seeing that the right kind of trees were planted and that they received the correct treatment during infancy. Careless planting, sometimes exclusively for ornamental purposes, and the belief that once the tree was put in it could be left to fend for itself against all the other forms of plant life struggling for existence on that particular piece of land, were responsible for the production of thousands of trees which have little or no commercial value. Nothing need be lost in the beauty of the park or plantation, and a great deal of economic value may accrue to society by the planning of tree planting, and by due care and attention to the saplings for the first ten or fifteen years.

By the eve of the Great War in 1914, the home producers were providing less than 10 per cent. of Britain's total requirements, and the rest was coming from the many sources of supply across the seas. The general organisation of the home industry was not particularly good, and there were a few who protested at the policy which left the future of the supply in the event of war so much to luck.

The 1914-1918 War opened with Britain's supplies completely at the mercy of the U-boat, and it was not very long before the shortage of shipping space caused a crisis. Committees were appointed and resolutions tabled, but it was really not until 1917—in the third year of the war—that the problem was taken in hand. Use of timber for a number of industries not essential to the war effort was banned, and something was done to restrict imports to those woods which were vital to the war effort. Home production was beginning to expand and it did reach a very creditable figure, for everywhere the axe was predominant, and no consideration was given to the problem of the best tree or the right aged tree to fell. All went down like wheat before the mower, and much of this felling in the early years of the war deprived a future generation of excellent timber without benefiting very appreciably those who so wantonly cut trees which' were often too small to be of any real value. Imports were reduced and the heavy demands of the armies on the Western Front were met to a great extent by the output of the French forests, aided by the various forestry units of the allied countries.

The first real step forward in forestry policy since the abortive Commission at the end of the eighteenth century was the appointment of the Acland Committee in 1916, charged with the job of examining and reporting on forestry policy. Sir Francis Acland, its Chairman, deserves well of his countrymen for the manner in which the Committee handled its evidence and produced its report. There have been some criticisms of the Committee, but it must not be forgotten that at the time it represented the first real attempt to put British forestry on the map, and it produced many constructive suggestions, which if they need modification in the light of present knowledge, lose nothing by that fact. Its terms of reference were "To consider and report upon the best means of conserving and developing the woodland and forestry resources of the U.K. having regard to the experience gained during the War." That experience was a painful one, and it might be imagined that the hard years of the war would teach all those concerned how dependent Britain was upon her home production of timber in the event of hostilities. Although the report and findings are now nearly 25 years old, a brief summary of the main decisions will help in understanding the policy pursued between the two wars. It must be remembered that these findings were published in 1918 and related generally to the period up to 1916.

i. It was estimated that the area covered by trees before the 1914 War was three million acres, yielding about forty-five million cubic feet—one third of the product that could have been realised from the same area if properly managed.

ii. Home production was less than one-tenth of imported timber. The cost of these imports in 1915 and 1916 was twice as much as in peace time and absorbed seven million net tons of shipping.

iii. The area used for rough grazing was estimated at between three and five million acres. At least two million acres could be devoted to forests with negligible damage to food production.

iv. Dependence on imported timber has proved a serious handicap in the conduct of the war. The U.K. cannot run the risk of future wars without safeguarding its supplies of timber as every other Power that counts has already done.

v. To exist in an emergency for three years, Britain must afforest 1,770,000 acres, two-thirds to be planted in the first forty years. In the first ten years, two hundred thousand acres to be planted, three-quarters by the State and one-quarter by private individuals assisted by the State. If the private individuals do more, the State can do less.

vi. No arable land is to be planted, but large areas at present almost waste will be used productively and help to give work to discharged soldiers.

vii. The suggested policy should give a return in pitwood after the fifteenth year; by the fortieth year there should be sufficient to keep the mines going for two years in an emergency.

   viii. The Forest Authority must have funds and powers to operate. Compulsory
           acquisition, if necessary, but fair compensation.
    ix. The Authority to make limited grants for each acre replanted in the first
           ten years, subject to approval of plans and conditions.
     x. Total cost for first ten years £3,425,000 and total of fifteen million pounds
           in forty years, after which the scheme should be self-supporting. This
           total is less than half the loss suffered during 1915-16 owing to dependence
           on imported timber.
    xi. The above is necessary for national safety. In addition, the virgin forests
           of the world are being steadily depleted and unless the large reserves of
           the Dominion of Canada are conserved, Britain should make even greater
           provision for home production than suggested above.

The Acland Committee probably took a far more gloomy view of
the situation than was justified, but they sat at a time when the full
effect of the submarine war was being felt and their pessimism is at
least understandable. Their desire to stress the urgency of the problem
was commendable and, if their statements had been taken more seriously,
a great deal of extra timber, particularly pit-props, might have become
available during the present war.

From the activities of the Acland Committee emerged the Forestry
Act of 1919 by which Commissioners were appointed and a fair measure
of budgetary support given to the work of the Forestry Commission.
But very soon afterwards financially embarrassed governments began to
cut down the allocations that had been given at the end of the war and
set a good example of giving with one hand and taking away with the
other. In 1922 the Geddes Committee actually recommended the
abolition of the Forestry Commission and in the end, although the
Commission was not completely abolished, financial support was cut,
and its activities had to be severely curtailed to fall into line with the
spirit of economy in national expenditure which was current at that
period of post-war history. Two years later, these decisions were
reversed, but already considerable harm had been done to the forestry
movement, and much of the good stimulated by the excellent work of
Acland and his committee was lost for ever. For the next six or eight
years, the Commission carried on its work more or less unhindered
and did manage to accomplish many of the tasks set for it in the early
days. But once more the financial stringency of the depression period
led to proposals to cut down the grants, and the Commission was asked
to make no further acquisitions and to restrict planting to a maximum
of 20,000 acres a year. During the first ten years of its life the Commission
had acquired on an average about 31,000 acres each year and had planted
a total of nearly 140,000 acres with suitable conifers and hardwoods.

This did not complete the work of the Commission since it had many
other duties, not the least important of which was the training of an
expert staff and the dissemination of useful information on forestry
and silvicultural problems to all those who sought its advice. Three
National Forest Parks—Snowdonia, Argyll and Dean—were purchased
and provide an effective monument to the work of the Commission
between the wars.

9

Despite the energetic efforts of the Commission, a great deal of useful timber land was incorrectly planted and the product of its soil lost for ever to the generations that followed. Bad cleaning of the land, the wrong kinds of trees planted, or the more serious feature of complete neglect of useful areas, have all contributed to lose for the nation an important economic asset which can never be entirely regained. Trees are a crop like any other agricultural product, and continuous neglect can cause the same loss as the derelict arable land which could be seen all over England and made the solution of Britain's food problem in war time so much more difficult.

During the post-war years, Britain continued to import large quantities of timber from all over the world, and the home producers were unable to increase their share of the market. They were short of raw material since the war years had reduced the usable trees; in any event, labour costs were sufficiently high to make it impossible to compete with the cheap imported supplies from the European countries and America.

Although Europe is an extensive timber-producing area, it still has to import part of its requirements from the North American continent even when the production of Soviet Russia is included. Europe as a whole imports from its constituent countries or from the North American continent about eighteen million tons of softwoods, of which about two million come from across the Atlantic. Of this grand total, Britain takes more than half—about ten million tons—and this is not because her demand is so much more enormous than other European industrial countries such as Germany, but because Britain has done less than the majority of great nations to provide for her own supplies from home production. Thus in Germany, very many thousands of tons are produced in the forest areas, and nearly one-and-a-half million persons are employed in the forest industries, which include, of course, all the sawmilling and woodworking branches of the trade. Germany is a much larger country than Britain, but the proportion of ten to one is nevertheless a striking illustration of the manner in which the Germans have concentrated upon their forest industries.

Many European countries are fortunate in the timber resources that they possess, and can look to large virgin forests stretching for miles across their territories as a source of economic strength and opportunity for development. To compare Britain, small and lacking in natural forest resources, with such countries would be unwarranted; yet even if Britain's acreage is set against that of those European States not richly endowed with vast space or virgin tracts, the comparison is distinctly unfavourable.

A timber-producing country such as Sweden has, as would be expected, a fairly large area under forests, amounting to nearly 60 per cent. of the whole. Germany has more than one-quarter of its surface covered with commercially usable trees, and the forests of France—a country which cannot be regarded as a timber producer proper—account for more than one-fifth of her land. Belgium, highly industrialised and with a very considerable density of population per acre, has about one-sixth of its area treed; even Holland and Denmark can boast proportions of nearly one-tenth of their areas. Against these figures the one-twentieth of Great Britain seems a miserable proportion, especially when it is remembered that about one-third of this area was classified by the Census of Woodlands in 1924 as being shrub or completely uneconomic woods of no commercial value whatsoever. Arable and grass lands were ten times as extensive as the area devoted to the production of marketable trees. Incidentally, the distribution between conifers and hardwood trees is now said to be about fifty-fifty, but this does not fully represent the position, since the hardwoods are in general more suitable for immediate felling and conversion than the softwoods. At the present time, it is the job of the authorities to raise the consumption of hardwoods since the annual increment—the amount of usable timber available each year—is higher because there are more hardwoods than softwoods, and it will take some years to right the balance.

No one can be surprised to find that up to the outbreak of war in 1939 supplies from abroad were flowing to this country in ever increasing quantities, and there were no signs of any desire to employ the woods from native trees. Many industrialists found that the imported material was so much more satisfactory for their purposes that no possible inducement could be offered which would make it worth their while to use home-produced timber. The sizes and manufacture, freedom from knots and general condition of the lumber that arrived from across the seven seas made many contemptuous of the inefficiently produced article available from British woodlands. There seemed very little chance that the home-produced wood would ever find users even if the enormous quantities needed could be produced.

One of the natural results of this lack of a healthy and well-developed forestry organisation has been the absence of up-to-date technical training or services. Such technical services are a concomitant of progressive forestry and not only were they absent but the other side of the trade, responsible for the marketing and importation of timber, showed little interest in forestry or timber technology, and itself suffered from a very low standard of scientific competence concerning the features and possibilities of the natural products it was handling in such vast quantity. Few sections of the industrial community can have been so ignorant of their subject and yet have survived the competition of substitute materials; and although the extent of home forestry operations did not justify a very large and expensive research service, the profits enjoyed by the distributors of all kinds were on a level which would, from motives of prudence alone, have warranted an attempt to educate a new generation in the science of forestry and timber utilisation.

This lack of interest on the part of the timber trade generally has

meant that the limited work which has been done was paid for from
Government grants to scientific bodies or was carried out by Government
institutions themselves. The scope of scientific research has thus been
limited and results produced which although valuable, might have
been extended and improved if a proportion of the not inconsiderable
profits earned by the trade had been set aside for research and training.

Under the Forestry Act of 1919, the Commissioners were empowered
to spend a part of their meagre resources on research and instruction
in order to encourage the spread of scientific forestry knowledge. Some
money has been spent, but the amount available did not justify the
creation of a whole host of experts, for the entire research programme
has averaged less than £11,000 each year from 1920, although in the
period immediately before the 1939 war, the expenditure on these
services was increasing. There are numerous opportunities for valuable
research work not only on forestry itself, the kinds of trees to grow,
where to plant them, how to treat them in their infancy and in the
years of maturity; there are also the equally important questions of
utilisation which have been stressed in a previous chapter.

Britain is so small that the right trees must be grown so that no square
yard of forest space is wasted by the planting of an unsuitable tree.
Not only the kind of tree—whether it shall be larch, ash, oak or Scots
pine—but the soil upon which it is proposed to plant must be taken
into consideration. Several scientists have turned their attention to
this subject, but in general the funds have been so limited that competition with the demands of agriculture and the greater importance of
that study have meant that most of the best scientific brains have been
obliged to concentrate upon other branches of soil research or ecology.
In addition to determining the nature of the trees there are to be grown
and the kinds of soil that suit them best, it is of prime interest to all
silviculturists to see that the trees are not hindered or destroyed during
growth by the action of insects, pests, fungi, animals or objectionable
parasites. A considerable number of trees in this country have suffered
from the attentions of one or other of these destroyers, and much natural
regeneration as well as nursery plantation work has thus come to nothing.

Because so much still remains to be done is not to belittle what
has already been accomplished by the few who have worked so energetically and continuously on the problems of the forests. Their
discoveries in soil research have made it possible in the last twenty years
to use as tree growing land two of the most unsatisfactory types of soil
to be found in this country—the peat and the upland heather clad soils.
This is a particularly important development since there are very considerable areas of both these kinds of land scattered throughout England
and Scotland, a great amount of which is useless for ordinary agricultural
purposes. A similar success was achieved by the French when they
planted and reared trees on the barren waste sand of the Landes area
and made it into one of the most profitable forestry plantations in

France. This was the culmination of many years of careful experiment, both with the kind of cultivation best suited to the soil and the types of trees that could be expected to grow on the bleak sandy coasts swept by Atlantic breezes.

The last and perhaps the most promising field for further research is the one already mentioned—to extend the scope of timber utilisation —and it is here that there must be complete co-operation between the forestry and silvicultural experts and those whose job it is to trade in and distribute timber. This will apply whether Britain remains a country importing 95 per cent. of its requirements or not; the important point is that those who derive the greatest advantages in monetary terms from the timber trade—the distributors—should make themselves responsible for this highly important branch of research, unless it can be financed on a large scale by the State, which in many respects would be more desirable. On the North American continent tremendous strides have been taken in providing funds for this kind of research, partly because of the greater interest of industrialists in new and revolutionary methods of production, and also because the greater elasticity of the educational system has made the development possible. American Universities and Colleges are more eager to undertake some obscure industrial investigation than their counterparts in this country —and they seldom lack the necessary funds to pursue the research.

In the international sphere, the most useful exchanges of forestry science and discussion have taken place at the British Empire Forestry Conferences and during the forestry proceedings of the various Imperial Conferences. Naturally, these proceedings have been limited to the consideration of inter-Empire forestry policy, but the technical side has received very detailed study. The results of some of these conferences are embodied in the two main technical organisations working in this country.

Empire Forestry Conferences were held in London in 1920, in Canada in 1923, in Australia and New Zealand in 1928, and in South Africa in 1935. A further conference arranged for late 1939 in India never took place because of the outbreak of war. In addition forestry subjects were well to the fore in the Imperial Conferences of 1926 and 1930, and the Imperial Economic Conferences of 1928 and 1932. The main general value of all these meetings was that they provided a forum at which timber problems could be discussed, even though the company was rather limited. As a result of the deliberations of the 1920 Conference, the Imperial Forestry Institute was established at Oxford in 1924 with the dual purpose of training forest officers and conducting research into forest production and, although excellent work has been done there, the Institute suffers from lack of funds and a certain detachment from the general organisation of the timber trade, the fault here not resting with the Institute. One year later there was established, under the general direction of the Department of Scientific and Industrial

Research, the Forest Products Research Laboratory at Princes Risborough which has proved itself to be of inestimable value to all engaged in the forestry and timber industries. Through its research and publications, the Laboratory has provided industry with a wealth of information, and is in fact the only scientific organisation in existence to answer the day-to-day queries on the vitally important raw material; their work needs not only further financial support but also the active collaboration of all branches of timber and forestry.

In the post-war period something more is required in addition to the exchange of views among members of the British Commonwealth. All producing and using countries must meet to discuss questions of future world supplies, forestry, silvicultural and soil matters, production and marketing organisation and the trend of new inventions in utilisation of timber and its products. There is sound reason to believe that some such world timber congress would be of great benefit to all participants, and probably lead to a reduction in international timber prices because of the more economic use of every stretch of timber-producing land throughout the world.

*   *   *   *   *   *

The plan to re-habilitate British forestry is set out in the Report of the Forestry Commissioners presented to Parliament in June, 1943. To understand its recommendations fully, six basic questions must be discussed and answered. These are:—

i. Is home produced timber likely to be satisfactory for the British market?
ii. Can sufficient be produced in view of the small total area of the country?
iii. Will agriculture suffer if forestry operations are extended?
iv. Is the private ownership of woodlands a stumbling block to any future scheme?
v. Will competition from abroad always make home production unprofitable?
vi. Is there room for improvement in the organisation of the home industry and the distributive services of the timber trade?

In the course of the story which has been told so far, here and there reference has been made to some points covered under the above six main heads; nevertheless it should now be possible to co-ordinate the whole and judge whether the Plan outlined in the Report is just workable, ideal or inadequate.

(*i*) In general, trees for conversion are needed in reasonably large sizes and as free as possible from defects which limit the strength or other properties of the wood. There is little scientific basis for the supposition that such trees cannot be grown in the British Isles, despite the wide variations in weather and soil conditions from one end of the islands to the other. The enormous stems found on the North American continent and the special types of hardwoods which are indigenous to a particular, usually a tropical area, cannot, of course, be expected to grow here; but there is no reason why many other species should not thrive under proper care and convert to suitable timber. Pit-props, which provide an outlet for the thinnings from plantations are equally good from this country as they are from Russia, France or Portugal, and plywoods can be made from many of the hardwoods such as beech, poplar and elm. The oaks, elms and beeches have already been mentioned as general utility woods, and they will grow as well here as in the United States, Czechoslovakia or Russia. Most of the difficulties which have accompanied their exploitation are due not to any inherent impossibility of nurturing them on British soil, but to other defects of production and preparation to be dealt with later. Several softwoods could be used as raw material for paper-making, although steps would have to be taken to increase planting of these particular timbers to justify the establishment of a paper-pulping and making industry over here. Other softwoods, such as larch, have a very wide scope of uses, and war has shown what can be done with this strong, hardy wood. Larch is not indigenous to this country, and an interesting story is told of its introduction into England. In the early part of the eighteenth century, some seedlings were brought here in flower pots and placed in a hothouse, where they promptly died. A few years later a similar experiment was tried but without much greater success, for the plants showed few signs of prospering and were thereupon put on to the dust heap. They were, however, not dead and in their new conditions began to thrive; this led to further experiments being carried out, some of which were successful. A few of the early seedlings were planted in the Churchyard at Dunkeld, and one larch tree still remains after more than two hundred years.

It must not be forgotten that until recently few trees were actually grown and tended with an eye to their eventual conversion into usable timber; therefore, no attempt was made to develop those qualities which were needed by industry. It was all a "hit or miss" affair—trees just grew, and if they grew well and were not too highly valued for ornamental purposes, the owner might one day cut them down, and this is the principal reason why the majority of trees do not produce either the quantity or the kind of timber that is required by this country. This is a difficulty which can be easily although not quickly overcome by experimenting with new species, the planned cultivation of the most suitable species and the careful tending of the trees from the sapling state until they are sufficiently mature for the woodcutter's axe. In this way useful trees could be grown yielding timber in many respects equal to similar species now reared in other climes and places.

(ii) The question of producing the right quality of timber has been answered; now it is natural to ask, is it possible to produce sufficient trees of the right type to make the effort worth while? This country is small, but even so the percentage of the total acreage under trees is much less than many other—and smaller—countries that have few of the natural advantages possessed by Britain. The first point which affects the total production a given piece of land can yield is the rate of growth of the trees planted, and, in the case of a number of softwoods at present to be found in this country, the rate of growth is much faster than in most other European countries. This is mainly due to the moist and equable climate of Britain, but is also dependent upon the trees being planted in soil suitable for the species in question. To maximise output, the first prerequisite is that the species should be carefully selected for rapid rate of growth and the soil in which each different species is planted should be right.

The total land area of Great Britain is approximately fifty-six million acres—about two-thirds making up England and Wales and one-third Scotland. Of this grand total, about forty-five million acres are used for all kinds of agriculture (including rough grazing), leaving eleven million for other purposes, roads, towns, marshes, forests and the rest. These figures are based upon the returns published in 1938 by the Ministry of Agriculture and, although the land under actual cultivation should perhaps be increased a little to cover the effects of the drive to produce more food during the war, this does not affect the grand total of forty-five million acres, since most of the extra land that has been ploughed since 1940 was not new, non-agricultural land being turned over, but grazing meadows coming under the plough. As a round figure then ten million acres are available for all the purposes that society and industry have other than agriculture. A very considerable proportion of this total is used up by towns and roads; for example, Greater London covers about half-a-million acres all told from one end to the other, and houses on that area one-fifth of the total population. The rest of the country has in general a lower average density, and a very rough calculation suggests that at least five million acres are used up by roads, factories, houses and buildings of all kinds over the country as a whole, leaving five million acres where trees might grow. The latest recorded figures of the area which contained any kind of timber whatsoever—including shrubs and devastated woodlands—was about three million acres, so that at least two million acres remain for afforestation.

It is difficult to say what the uses of this considerable area are, but even a casual observer can see large tracts not covered with any satisfactory vegetation. Perhaps such lands need draining before they would grow trees; or the soil is very poor and would have to be improved to enable even the most hardy trees to thrive. Whatever the reason, it is not a wild assertion to make that *some* of this land could probably be brought into use if there was a market for the products to be grown upon it. This is the kind of problem that faces a Government after every war, and whether any action is taken depends upon the extent to which other demands conflict with the expenditure necessary to rehabilitate this undeveloped land. It is obvious that a great deal of erstwhile cultivable land has been allowed to go out of use during the past hundred and fifty years, and it will be no easy matter to bring these areas back into profitable cultivation either for ordinary agriculture or for the growing of trees.

Yet there is another category of the land of Britain which could be made to provide space for planting trees—the rough grazing land consisting of about sixteen million acres which was included in the figure of forty-five million acres of agricultural land. This is land which is found throughout Great Britain but mainly in the hill country of England and Scotland; its main uses today are for sheep grazing and in some parts of Scotland for deer forest. It is unlikely that to encroach upon this would seriously interfere with food production either now or in the future, since much of the land is not regularly used for grazing and is put to no economic purpose whatsoever. It would only serve in a few cases as suitable for ordinary agricultural land, and those parts which are not actually being used for sheep grazing would go to make up a reserve of land to be drawn on for afforestation, if the State so wished.

No satisfactory estimate of the plantable area of Great Britain has been made, but the Forestry Commission suggest that some five million acres could be developed for forestry work. This would bring Britain's percentage of forest land up to 9 per cent. to exceed the figures of countries like Holland and Denmark, but still leave her well behind Belgium, France and Germany. France, for example, with a total area more than twice as great as this country has over twenty-six million acres under forests.

What emerges from all these figures? The main point is that Britain is far behind many of her neighbours in the development of her forest lands; that although her area is small, there exists a reserve of potentially good land for forestry; and that given the right kind of soil research and silviculture, Britain could greatly increase the physical production of timber. Whether it would *pay* her to do so is not for the moment the question under review, but she could plant, if it was necessary, at least up to double her present area.

(*iii*) The third question follows naturally from the considerations which have just been discussed; to what extent would the expansion of tree planting affect the food production of this country? It has already been mentioned that there is a considerable area of rough grazing land, part of which could be brought into timber production, and this factor goes to the root of the whole question. In 1940 the Forestry Commission undertook an interesting investigation to discover exactly how much food and other agricultural produce would be lost by the planting with trees of a certain area which previously was used as grazing land for sheep. The results, based upon careful calculations of the sheep yield and the timber to be produced from the land taken over, showed that a very much greater weight of timber could be grown on this land than the yield of mutton and wool. Naturally, the weight of the several commodities is not a fair method of deciding whether it would be advisable to switch over; for such a decision could be more securely made by comparing the average costs of the two productions and the value of the annual yields. In war time, however, different considerations dominate policy, and it may well be that since the really scarce commodity is shipping space, to prepare to produce the larger tonnage of timber at the expense of the smaller tonnage of mutton and wool is the wise step to take. Obviously, in the middle of a war it would be an act of foolishness to forgo the immediate but smaller quantity of mutton in exchange for the larger quantity of timber in forty odd years' time, by which date, it is to be hoped, the need would have gone as the war would no longer be on. This does not mean to say that after the war the experiment would be useless, for it might be an insurance against a similar crisis happening at some later date, even if the most optimistic view of the future is taken.

The full exploitation of the land of Britain has not yet been achieved, and until it is possible to say that every acre taken for forestry operations means an acre less for agriculture, the utilisation of land is still incomplete and, what is more, the difficult problem whether to replace food and wool by timber does not arise. If full use of resources is reached, it is not even then certain that it will always pay to grow food in preference to timber; only the comparative values at the time can influence the decision. It is perhaps not fully appreciated by agriculturists that an acre of normally good land will produce timber at somewhere in the region of one-and-a-half tons per annum, although naturally this product is not immediately realisable but must be taken as a total yield when the trees reach maturity. The general accumulation of product is of this order of magnitude, and is, as it were, stored up in the growing tree until the moment comes for it to be felled and the full value released. A similar piece of land if utilised for ordinary agriculture would be producing a fair crop if it yielded one ton of corn, but in this case it all comes within one year and is immediately enjoyed. Leaving aside other considerations such as labour costs, by-products and relative prices, it is possible to envisage circumstances when the use of this acre of land for timber production might be justified. These facts are given not to suggest that good wheat land should become a tree plantation but to counteract the erroneous belief that come what may, it is always the agriculturists who must have the land for crops and not the forester for trees.

It is not possible to give a clear answer to the question concerning the reduction in food production which timber output would cause, since everything depends upon the extent to which the planting of trees is pushed. No survey has clearly established the amount of lower grade land which is available for forestry work, and until such a survey has been made, it is reasonable to assume on the basis of known facts that a considerable area of land could be planted with trees without causing a serious decline in the food-growing potential. A certain area could be so employed immediately without interfering in any way with agriculture, and the first step would be to locate this type of land and bring it into the forestry scheme. When the stage has been reached at which every new acre used for forestry is an acre taken from agriculture, the distribution between the two uses must depend upon the prevailing economic and political situation.

(*iv*) The fourth question should if possible not be treated as a political issue but be answered in the light of what private ownership has done for the British forests in the past and to what extent it can, without undue help from the State, provide for the future. The issue then is—have the private woodland owners done all within their power to conserve and develop forest wealth during the last fifty years, and are they capable of maintaining a satisfactory scheme of development in the years to come without becoming a charge on the national exchequer?

Until the establishment of the Forestry Commission, all forests were privately owned with the exception of a few Crown lands, and today it is true to say that the majority of the woodlands of this country are in the hands of private owners, and only in a few cases are these estates developed and cared for as potential timber-producing lands. Whatever the reasons for inaction in each particular case, the facts are that the private owners, with some notable exceptions, have not found it worth their while to treat the production of timber-yielding trees as an important function. Some of the causes of this lack of interest in the future of their property have already been mentioned, such as the fact that a woodland investment takes an average of thirty-five years to yield a return, and owners prefer to put their resources into something that will give them a quicker profit. A second strong reason for inactivity has been the lack of inducements to prepare a crop of timber, with prices low and the market situation disorganised. Thirdly, owners have rarely had the technical knowledge necessary to equip them for the difficult job of silviculture. Lastly, many owners have but relatively small forest areas, and it has never seemed worth their while to spend time and money on them. It must also be remembered that a considerable acreage of potentially useful woodlands has been regarded as "untouchable" as a reserve for ornamental or sporting purposes, which is perhaps the very worst reason for failure to develop.

It would be unfair to allege that the woodland owners have prevented the progressive exploitation of the national forests without first examining the concomitants of a successful policy and seeing how far the owners have fallen short of implementing this policy. The land must be prepared for planting and the correct kinds of trees planted with due regard to the type of soil, climatic conditions and the country's demand for various species of timber; this is the first stage in the job of successful forestry. The second stage demands the application of considerable care and attention to the young trees, so that they thrive and are not destroyed by pests or by neglect in the nursery stage. A great deal of useful timber can be lost for ever by failure at this stage; but this care of the young trees is once again a duty which cannot be carried out unless the owners are ready to undertake the expenditure of money on expert advice,

foresters and the necessary equipment. As soon as the trees are old
enough to be thinned out, the thinnings—which are quite valuable even
in normal times—must be taken away, and the land generally tended
so that the trees left can have the greatest possible chance of survival
and growth. Next the estate must be cleared of fellable trees at the
right moment and lastly—and perhaps most important—the cleared
areas must be re-planted at a suitable time with new trees, so that the
ground does not become covered with wild undergrowth and eventually
prove useless for forestry operations.

It will be readily appreciated that the complete process is both
lengthy and expensive, so that the owner must plan ahead for the expenditure of his capital including the provision of the best expert advice and
attention for the growing trees. At every stage, there is money going
out without any income emerging until a much later date—perhaps
in some cases forty or fifty years ahead—and in addition every type of
technical problem will be encountered from the date that the plants
are removed from the nursery until they are grown trees ready for the
woodman's axe. Is it therefore very surprising that only the few amongst
woodland owners have been either willing or able to provide the finance
and the technical skill which success demands? Small wonder, then
that there are many tracts of timber lands which have been spoiled
beyond recall by bad forestry work, neglect or ignorance. Many forest
owners have started well enough only to find in ten or twenty years
that they must sell the land for other purposes, or for numerous reasons
their financial position does not enable them to refuse a tempting offer
that they have received to sell the land for building or, as it is sometime
called, "development"? To take the most charitable view, the owners
can hardly be blamed for their inability to develop the land as forestry
capital, for the job that society has given them is not one which a private
individual can do with the resources at his disposal. The State is the
only body that can plan wisely which areas are to be devoted to forestry
development, the only authority capable of providing the necessary
finance and waiting long periods for a return on its investment; and the
State is the most suitable vehicle for providing the required technical
skill at a reasonable figure and maintaining research organisations to
keep abreast of new ideas and methods from all the world's timber
producers. There is one further advantage which the State has which
would be enjoyed by private individuals only if they were co-operatively
organised. The skilled workers available can be spread over a number
of estates so that the value of each one of them is maximised. In forestry
operations, ten men may be needed on one estate but they are not fully
employed for the whole year, but if these same ten men were able during
slack times to transfer their activities to other areas—a transfer which
the State could well arrange—the production would be cheaper in
labour costs and could therefore compete more effectively with imports
than under present conditions.

The fact that the forestry organisations all demand for their members financial assistance, freedom from death duties and excess profits taxes as well as remissions from general State charges which other branches of industry have to bear, suggests that the function of carrying on a satisfactory forest development policy is not possible without the intervention of the State. Is it not therefore far better that this should be clearly vested in the State authority and not be a half-and-half compromise which is doomed to failure? The people have found everywhere that public services such as roads and railways can really only be efficiently operated by State bodies. They are too large and important to the everyday life of society to be left to the whims and fancies of private control, especially since their very nature tends to encourage combination and monopoly. The forest lands of Britain demand similar treatment. Small, straggling areas are no use; the whole problem must be treated as one and the most suitable areas planted with trees according to a carefully prepared plan. To this kind of policy private ownership, however enlightened, must always be a stumbling block.

(v) In trying to answer the fifth question—will competition from abroad always ruin home producers—there is a danger of becoming mixed up in the whole tariff tangle. It is therefore better to confine the answer to a consideration of the facts of the case, whether any kind of protection is justified or required, whether world shortage may not solve the whole problem and as a final point whether future Governments may desire to protect and expand forestry for reasons which are not economic. First of all the facts.

Britain has for many years imported the greater proportion of her needs at prices which were so low that requests were put forward by the home trade for a duty on imported timber, an application rejected on the grounds that the trade was not really in a position to supply the home market with the quantity it needed at fair prices. There are very few who would argue with the decision of the Import Advisory Committee on this question; but there would be more reason to give the home industry some measure of protection if at the same time it was reorganising itself and taking steps to produce the quantity and quality of timber required by the consumers. In other words, it could claim the right to be regarded as an "infant industry" to be nursed and protected for a number of years during which time it would have the chance of growing into a healthy manhood. This is perhaps the only economically sound basis for protecting the home industry, although there are probably many who would be prepared to go very much farther and give subsidies and preferences to keep the production going; such decisions must remain in the hands of the Government of the country at the time, and it is difficult to say now if circumstances will justify protection at some future date. The protectionist school favour arrangements similar to those covered by the Wheat Quota Act, since timber is in an analogous position in that the full quantity cannot be produced but only a relatively small proportion. Any such scheme would have to allow for the fact that today there is very little raw material in the form of growing trees and in the future this stock is likely to increase slowly. It is difficult to envisage any great enthusiasm for quota schemes in view of their limited success in the past and the economic and political régime with which their name is inevitably associated.

In addition to the clear issue of protection or no protection, it is possible to imagine a post-war situation in which many of the main exporting countries are so busy reconstructing their bomb and war-damaged lands that they need a great proportion of their timber supplies themselves, and the total entering international trade may well decrease for a number of years. This would take the form of an increase in world prices, and in such circumstances the home producer should be able to compete effectively with the foreign supplier, and if he does the job properly might lay the foundations of an efficient industry. It must not, however, be forgotten that even if such favourable conditions prevail after the war their duration will be limited, and at the same time the home industry will have to work poor supplies of raw material due to the limited pre-war planting and the excessive fellings of the war period. There is little evidence of a prospective world shortage due to a general dwindling of supplies, since today practically every nation important as timber producers has safeguarded its future output by afforestation laws, measures to ensure a "sustained yield" from the forests and to increase fire protection and pest control. The shortage will be temporary only and due to the abnormal consumption required to rebuild rapidly so many of Europe's cities, towns and villages. The quickest remedy, as in 1919, will be to make timber dwellings and erect them in large numbers in a matter of months. This must limit international trade in timber as it did with Russia who was some years before she recommenced exporting timber after the last war, although her situation was peculiar and complicated by the Revolution and the interventionist wars against her. The other European exporters have suffered very severely at the hands of Germany, both as regards war damage by occupation and indiscriminate felling of their trees, and it seems unlikely that countries such as Finland, Poland, Esthonia, Latvia, Czechoslovakia and Yugoslavia—whatever their political boundaries and allegiances—will be able to commence the export of their timber just where they left off when the war started.

The third factor is the possibility that the Government of the day may decide to encourage forestry, although not on a truly economic basis, with the intention of aiding rural industries and putting men back into healthy employment. This will surely mean that they will so subsidise the industry as to make it a paying proposition unless, of course, they choose to take it over altogether and run it as a State concern; all this will be governed by the kind of planning which emerges as a result of the lessons learnt in the war. The lack of balance visible in the geographical distribution of both population and industry since 1918 suggests that all available land will in future be utilised, and the movement towards the bigger towns checked by opening up some of the hitherto undeveloped countryside. The drift from the South-West to the South-East and from North to South generally had become a menace to the proper organisation of society on this small island and great areas of Britain, capable of development, were marked off as "depressed areas", later to be known by the more refined term "special areas". Forestry is not by any means the main method of righting this lack of balance, but it would at least be one way of improving natural resources and provide worth-while and healthy work for many needy families. Much will depend upon the kind of society that the Government wishes to create, the resources they are prepared to devote to the work and the wisdom they exhibit in carrying out their plans. It is to be hoped that in planning a better Britain the case for employing a certain proportion of the total land area on forestry will receive careful consideration. If it is decided to encourage forestry for these reasons, which are, on the surface, non-economic ones, it must mean as a start protection or subsidies in one form or another. Here again the State could be expected to administer more efficiently and at less cost than a host of private individuals who might look upon the State merely as a means of making their businesses more profitable.

(vi) The sixth and last question concerns home production and the distributive trades as they were organised up to the outbreak of war. Has the war taught those responsible any lessons which by improving organisation would lead to a more satisfactory method of getting the timber from the sawmills where it is cut to the man on the job who actually uses the wood?

The normal peace time organisation of marketing was built up not upon the function of distributing home supplies but to handle the ever increasing quantities of imported timber which were arriving from all the world producers. It had therefore all the features of an international market, with brokers and agents, merchants and importers, many of whom never handled the timber in any shape or form and dealt only in the "paper" or documentary claim to the goods. The majority of these people did carry out an economic function in that they provided finance or were responsible for bringing together one who had a claim on a shipload of timber with another who wanted that cargo; yet some of them had very little expert knowledge and would have found it impossible to identify different kinds of timber or to give any useful technical advice to actual users. Such middlemen did very well out of the industry in comparison with the little that they put into it. An agent or merchant who opens up the trade of some outlandish corner of the earth and brings to the users in this country goods which satisfy a real need is doing something for society and in present circumstances deserves his reward. But the agent who buys a set of documents, a claim upon some physical merchandise, from one bank and, after taking a commission, sells them at once to another bank, is not discharging any service to the community but is only enhancing the price to be paid ultimately by the actual consumer.

The total effect of this badly organised distribution is to increase the costs of the raw material to industry beyond the justifiable level and make the competition of substitutes more difficult to meet. There are two alternative policies to improve the situation—either to combine or to co-operate. Combination, even if it were possible in a sphere of commerce where the pirate proudly calls himself a rugged individualist, would ultimately lead to serious abuses such as price ringing, control of supply and flouting of consumers' wishes up to the point where substitutes begin to operate. What is really needed is a co-operative organisation capable of maximising the value of the labour force available, using capital more economically and minimising the cost of the timber to the consumers. Naturally, side by side with these changes must go the increased technical competence which is so vital to survival.

These considerations are in the main relevant to the handling of imports; the problem of changing the chaotic conditions which persisted before the war in the home production side of the industry is even more difficult.

The main need is for proper marketing arrangements so that the native woods have at least some chance against the imported timbers. The best type of market—on the assumption that the present economic system is still in existence—would be created by having two categories of operators. In the first place, the sawmills, with their host of technical problems to meet and solve and concentrating upon their big job of production, cannot be expected to understand the complications of marketing their products. These functions can be left to another category of operators—call them merchants—who would be responsible for ascertaining the needs of industry, advising upon questions of the type and quality of material to use for a particular job, and any other technical matters where their skilled knowledge of the qualities and virtues of wood can be satisfactorily used. They could then give to the sawmills all necessary advice on production questions, and on what to produce to meet industry's demand.

To anyone accustomed to the gay chaos of the pre-war period this must seem like a Utopian change indeed; yet the plain fact is that without economic and technical reorganisation the production and distribution of timber in this country will never be carried out in the manner most likely to benefit both the timberman and the community. Post-war Governments will be neither so foolish nor corrupt as to ladle out the taxpayers' money to industries without some assurance that efficiency is being achieved; if industry gets in first with its plans it is likely to gain in the end. With increased efficiency in the home production of timber, it will be possible to compete with foreign producers even if only to a limited extent, and if in addition there is provided some guarantee of the supplies of trees, it will justify the foundation of a structure large and strong enough to maintain itself and expand as the years unfold.

*   *   *   *   *   *

The discussion of these six questions has disclosed the vital points which the future legislators must watch. In the new order of things, forestry will have some part to play and for that reason, if for no other, the Plan outlined by the 1943 Report of the Forestry Commissioners will be the basis upon which a future Minister of Reconstruction will begin to work. The Report deals mainly with the structure of British forestry over the last forty odd years and within their terms of reference and carefully avoiding any departure from accepted principle, the Commissioners have done a competent job. Many might have wished that the members had applied to the work ideas more in keeping with the needs of the post-war era, for in fact no one reading the Report in 1919 instead of 1943 would have found anything very revolutionary in it. There are no violent breaches of traditional economic theory, no suggested changes in social legislation and no affront to vested interests.

The Report sums up in its own words the prerequisites of any plan as follows:—

"The post-war position will demand speedy and large-scale action. The requisites for success are available. British conditions are suitable for the rapid growth of good timber, there is sufficient land available in the existing woodlands and uncultivated rough grazings, many useful improvements have been made during the inter-war period in the technique of forestry, the Forestry Commission has acquired large-scale administrative experience of the problems and has a staff of well-trained forest officers and foresters. It is hoped also that private owners will continue to play an important part in securing the Nation's timber supplies."

The Plan proposed by the Report recommends the planting of five million acres with trees during the next fifty years, some three million in excess of the present area under forests. This is regarded as a minimum for national safety and should also meet any shortage in the future due to a world shrinkage of supplies. It is suggested that this area must not just be planted; it must be managed and developed to yield the maximum product. The three million acres will be forested on bare ground over the next five decades, and in choosing the land all the considerations already mentioned will be borne in mind. The total area is calculated eventually to supply Britain with some 35 per cent. of all her timber requirements and to cost the country just over forty-one million pounds net in the first decade—some four millions per year. With the plan will go the building up of a body capable of efficient management, a scheme of correct planting and replanting, systematic marketing and utilisation, the development of suitable transport in the forest areas and the settlement of forest workers in dwellings in their proper surroundings. Much of the groundwork for the attainment of

10

these aims has already been done by the Forestry Commission in its past labours; but there will still remain a great deal to do to accomplish the Plan.

The ticklish question of State or private forestry causes the greatest difficulties. That part of the two million odd acres which is now privately owned will remain so but much of it will, it is hoped, be "dedicated" for forestry purposes; or if the owners prefer it, acquired by the State Forestry Authority. There will then be three categories of forest lands —State owned, privately owned but "dedicated", and privately owned but not "dedicated". The State forests will be acquired by purchase and managed in a manner similar to the present practice of the Forestry Commission, and the extent of this acquisition will depend as before upon the degree of financial support afforded by the Government to the State Authority. There is to be no forced acquisition, although powers would presumably exist to take over estates with due compensation.

The second class of forest lands are those to be dedicated by the owners to the State and in the words of the Report, land so dedicated "could not thereafter be diverted to other uses except for approved reasons; dedication in effect would bind the land and would be unaffected by changes in ownership". The owner would undertake to use the land in such a manner that timber production was the main object, to keep to a plan as set out by the Forestry Authority, to employ skilled supervision and to keep proper accounts of all the forestry activities. In return for this undertaking, the State would provide financial assistance, which it is suggested should be at the rate of 25 per cent. of annual expenditure, in addition to which there would be facilities for borrowing money from the Forestry Authority for expending on approved activities. If and when the estate became self-supporting, the financial aids would cease. It should be stressed that such dedication is a purely voluntary act on the part of the woodland owner.

The third category covers the woodlands privately owned but not dedicated; these will receive no financial assistance so that the position remains as it is today, but technical advice would be available free to all those who sought it.

Is it a good Plan? There is little wrong with it so far as it goes, but that the limited proposals will meet the full needs of a post-war Britain is unlikely. Yet with the experience of what followed the last Report in 1918, to achieve even what is set out in the Plan would be something of a victory. The total production that will emerge when the whole scheme has had time to fructify cannot be fixed, and it seems a little optimistic to talk of 35 per cent. of Britain's requirements being met. By comparing the output of other countries with the area they have under trees, it seems that five million acres will not suffice to produce each year some seven hundred thousand standards of softwoods. The cost figures are also open to question on the general grounds that they are computed on the basis of present day prices, whereas it is fairly certain that after the war changes in the price level will make nonsense of all such cost calculations. In view of this fact, the annual charge must be taken as a very rough estimate of cost as otherwise it is misleading.

The main criticism of the Plan rests upon the basis of the provisions for the control and acquisition of land. The past activities of the Commission have shown beyond any question that the only sound method of developing forestry operations in this country is to have reasonably large areas under the direct control of the State Authority so that supervision is complete and labour economised. The new scheme for "dedication" has serious faults since it leaves outside any owners who refuse either to sell, dedicate or privately plant their lands—and there are many large landowners who will be adamant. These areas are so extensive and their importance to Britain so great that they must give up their ownership if the forests are to be developed. The Government of the day cannot prepare its programme if the land it is to control is governed by the vagaries of each individual owner—some particularly suitable piece of land may be required, but the owner will neither dispose of the site nor agree to "dedicate". There is but one solution; the needs of society must override those of the individual landowner and the site must be acquired to take its place in the general plan. In such a small country as this, the reconstruction Government *must* decide what areas are to be built upon, what land is to be farmed and what land is to be used for afforestation.

As early as the end of the eighteenth century, Thomas Paine and Thomas Spence were advocating the communal ownership of land so that the full potentialities of the soil could be enjoyed by the people. More recently, Lord Addison, an accepted authority on land and agriculture, wrote in his book, *A Policy for British Agriculture*:—

> "Only under National ownership, and with the consideration of plans alongside the proper examination of other possible uses of the Land, as well as the relation thereto of the claims of beauty and amenities, can a satisfactory forestry policy be made possible."

Discharged soldiers will need work and homes: the country must develop all its natural resources to the full. No one must be permitted to remain outside the main scheme, since the so-called sacred rights of private property do not give anyone the freedom to sabotage the community's interests because these conflict with his own. The owner whose land is scheduled for development cannot refuse or make his acceptance conditional upon receiving grants from the other members of society, for by failing to act as he is bid he has given up whatever rights society granted him to possess the land. A post-war Britain can hardly afford the luxury of citizens who have no duties to their fellow men yet claim inalienable pensions because of their ancient, threadbare "rights". In describing the part played by private owners Sir Roy Robinson, Chairman of the Forestry Commission, who can hardly be described as a revolutionary, said in an address to the Chartered Surveyors' Institution in 1938:—

"(many owners) are indifferent so long as the woods provide a cover for game or are ornamental" or " . . . just don't care whether their woods contribute anything towards the well-being or safety of the nation."

His wide experience of examining land for planting and acquisition gives to his views an authority that compels attention.

Forestry must be treated with the same seriousness as town planning, location of industry or the organisation of roads and highways—as one of the big scale undertakings which cannot be left to the piecemeal work of a hundred private individuals, however much goodwill they may display. The competing claims of agriculture and forestry can only be justly and correctly settled if the country is treated as one unit and decisions made which pay due regard to the interests of the nation in its entirety. On this basis, it is probable that the total plantable area could be greatly increased, possibly up to about eight million acres, by rehabilitating low grade land and employing the less valuable stretches of rough grazings now not fully utilised by agriculture.

Sir George Stapledon has estimated that from some of the rough and hillside grazings the yield of meat is no more than five to fifteen pounds weight per annum per acre, and the hill farms using the rough grazings average about fourteen pounds. He estimates, too, that very rough pastures could yield, with periodic re-ploughing and re-grassing, up to one hundred pounds per acre per annum, a product which could certainly be exceeded both in weight and value if timber were grown instead. Another authority writes:—

"There are millions of acres of land well suited for timber production on commercial lines that are at present entirely waste."

It is not difficult to envisage the great expansion of amenities that the people of this country would enjoy from these new forest areas quite apart from the economic advantages to accrue at a later date.

For these reasons, the Forestry Report Plan is not sufficient to meet the needs of a nation bent upon re-planning its resources and determined to exact from the "original and indestructible qualities of the soil" the maximum produce which adequate capital and labour, combined with the unlimited inventiveness of science, can wring from an uncharitable Nature. It is dangerous to over-stress the importance of forestry to the community and misleading to set at too high a figure the possible plantable area. But for future statesmen to ignore the fund of public weal that can be derived from the soil of Britain would be a signal failure to discharge one of the fundamental duties of government.

The debate in the House of Commons which followed the publication of the Report was a dismal affair, and few members seemed to have grasped the significance of forestry operations or sufficiently understood the Report to offer any constructive criticisms. If the mighty problems of reconstruction after the war are to be debated with this air of unreality, the future is indeed black. Sir George Courthope, the Forestry Commission's representative in the House and himself a signatory of the Report, detailed sections from the Report without contributing anything vital to the debate. It was perhaps unfortunate that this important subject should have been introduced by one so singularly devoid of progressive ideas; it at least demonstrated clearly the need for new and ·inspired management of British resources if post-war progress is to be achieved. The debate took on a slightly Gilbertian air when Sir George summed up with the five essentials of administrative success. Four he gave: but unhappily the fifth must remain forever denied to the legislators of the Mother of Parliaments—for Sir George mislaid the paper on which he had written the fifth point and could not remember what it said! His case was that the private owners had failed to develop their woodlands in past years, but that if the country was to get the timber that it needed, the owners must nevertheless be supported, financed, helped and generally nursed. In every branch of life, those who fail so miserably to discharge their duties receive less gentle treatment; in fact the individualists' creed is based upon the "survival of the fittest", or, at least, naming as "the fittest" those who do succeed in surviving.

There were a few members who gave the country's case rather than that of the landowners and some found the estimate of plantable land, low though it is in the Report, far too high. These members were mainly the advocates of the agriculturists, and they threw out dark hints of the competition between agriculture and forestry that would follow the implementing of the Plan. The Minister Without Portfolio, Sir William Jowett, carefully poised himself upon the pin point, leaving the hands of the Government free to accept or refuse the Report but not dealing with its provisions in detail. Sandwiched between this eloquent legal skirmishing and bland tributes to the members of the Forestry Commission came another eulogy of private owners which would have sounded like obsequiousness from the mouth of a less eminent member; it is worth putting the passage on record:—

"Private owners have played a distinguished part in the past. If it had not been for the private owner at the present time, we should indeed be in a nasty position. Though the general standard of forestry has not, taken on the whole, been high, yet there have been some very notable exceptions. . . . I said that the general standard had not been high . . ."

It is seldom that posterity rewards with honourable mention those who have done so little to deserve it. In actual fact, Britain *was* in a "nasty position" in this war and need not have been if the owners in the pre-1914 period had done their work adequately. When the time comes to publish the full story, it will be seen that the Minister Without Portfolio can hardly have been fully conversant with the facts, otherwise his praise of the owners might have been somewhat modified. The appropriate officials might even be able to tell him of resistance encountered from owners when felling of their estates was requested in the interests of the nation; details of the number of compulsory felling orders issued might have shown that not all those possessing growing trees realised the crisis of timber supplies and knew where their duty lay. The use of the compulsory felling order was probably very much restricted, as compulsory orders have always been in Britain's history, and therefore even if the number was large it would not fully represent the measure of opposition which had to be overcome.

The suggested conflict between agriculture and forestry was perhaps magnified in the debate as although it is an issue of the greatest importance, until the whole of Britain's soil resources have been closely surveyed and decisions taken as to which land is suitable for each purpose, no reliable quantitative statement can be made. What has been called a "Doomsday Book of the Soil" is badly needed so that every acre is mapped according to the soil of the land and the suitability of the various soils for agricultural purposes. The staffs will be available after the war and the job need not take very long. Many writers have advocated this step, and Mr. S. L. Bensusan in one of his articles underlines the need for scientific soil mapping by telling the following story. A farmer wished to purchase a few hundred acres of land in the south of England for fruit growing, but before finally deciding upon a certain piece of land, he obtained an expert's report upon the soil. This showed that out of the area of two hundred acres, only ten were suitable for fruit growing, although the rest of the land would support other types of crops quite satisfactorily. No one would be expected to spend a few thousand pounds on sinking a coal-mine shaft without a geologist's survey proving the existence of a coal seam; yet farmers everywhere take over land without any clear evidence of what its virtues or vices are.

With the structure of each land area ascertained, proper use can be made of every acre, and it is not begging the question to feel confident that if this survey were made, forestry would be allocated further areas for development.

During the debate the Government spokesmen indicated their desire to hear more of the private owners' point of view, and the Forestry Commission published a supplementary Report some six months later with details of meetings that had been held jointly with representatives of the Forestry Societies and the Landowners' Associations. The landowners did not find the suggested financial assistance satisfactory and new grants were decided upon. They also felt that insufficient credit had been given to them for the part they played in providing the trees for the war effort despite years of State neglect. The tributes paid in Parliament should have been more than sufficient to share around among those woodland owners who had deserved well of their country.

The rest of the proceedings covered small details such as the careful defining of words in the original Report which might be construed as giving the Forestry Commission power to confiscate. It is remarkable how anxious many of these woodland owners are to hold on to property which, according to their oft-stated protestations, has been nothing but an expensive burden and a heavy drain upon their finances for many years past. It was also decided that the owner must be given "a reasonable time" to make up his mind whether he will dedicate or plant his land before the State steps in and acquires it. It is essential that this period is clearly defined as otherwise there may be wholesale obstruction, and delays similar to those which accompanied attempts to acquire slum property for re-housing in peace time.

It must be concluded that the Forestry Commission Plan will not do much to rehabilitate British woodlands, although it may add a few hundred thousand acres to the existing forestry area. The necessary measures likely to meet the demands of the post-war period can be summed up as follows. The Ministry of Agriculture by a soil survey can decide where forestry areas could be established if other conditions were favourable, and the Forestry Commission must have powers of immediate acquisition of any or all of the areas thus chosen. If it is satisfied that any particular area is a suitable unit and efficiently conducted, acquisition may be unnecessary, although the owner must conform to the general plan. How the land acquisition is arranged and what this planting and development plan will be must remain for detailed consideration in the light of existing conditions and the claims of competing economic activities; but the principles governing the broad scheme can be thus stated.

*   *   *   *   *   *

The history of forestry in this country has been briefly related: it is certainly not a chronicle of great achievement. The mistakes of the past were largely of omission, for few have been willing to espouse the cause of home timber supplies for the last 150 years. Today there is a different spirit abroad and if those responsible for reconstruction are wise, they will sense this change and put forestry high up on their list of new industries for the Britain of tomorrow. Whatever the length of the war, home supplies are already seriously devastated, and years of work lie ahead to replant the raw materials for future industrial generations. Despite the obvious defects of the new Forestry Commission Plan, it is a foundation upon which much can be built if enlightened statesmanship translates its hesitating proposals into a vigorous scheme of development of latent resources for the benefit of communities yet to take shape. The case for producing some part of consumption from home supplies has been made; and with its achievement will come healthy work for many and increased amenities for all. Let those who have the power to change the fortune and the face of Britain for the better act with resolve.

> "Thus from all these instances, we may gather th
> necessity of a more than ordinary knowledge, requisite i
> such whose profession obliges them that deal in timbe
> to study the art well; nor is it a small stock of philosophy
> to skill in the nature and property of these materials, an
> which does not only concern architects, but the
> subsidiary, carpenters, joyners, especially wood-broker
> etc."
>
> JOHN EVELYN: *Sylv*

CHAPTER V

OUT OF THE WOOD

IN THE early days of the war, a book was published in the Unite
States which set out to prove that the industrial plans of Goering wer
based upon the use of wood for all purposes, and that much of th
territory over which Germany desired to exercise dominion was wante
mainly because of its timber supplies. In other words, it was said tha
if the Nazis could obtain control of the timber resources of Europe
they would soon be able to dominate the whole world. At base th
idea is sound, but the implications were stretched rather too far. Wha
the Nazis did believe was that if their plants capable of producin
numerous materials from wood had enough capacity, they should b
able to do without many of the imports which the British blockad
would keep from them in the early days of the war, and for this purpos
Austria, Czechoslovakia and Poland were acquisitions of the highes
value.

Thus in the last three or four decades, the importance to man o
wood as an industrial raw material has undergone a complete change
In the very early days, the tree was used in the form of a trunk and worke
to the simple requirements of primitive society; later it was sawn int
boards and planks to meet more detailed needs. Now it is emergin
as a fully manufactured material, in the form of thin sheets of plywoo
or plastic substances or chemicals of many kinds.

The tree is the basis of all these materials, and it possesses two grea
advantages over nearly every other type of raw material. In the firs
place, man can plan so that there will still be trees when iron ore, coa
and oil have been cleaned from every crevice of the earth's surface. Th
second advantage is that whereas the minerals must be accepted as the
are found, it is now possible to produce, within reasonable limits, th

type of wood required for a particular purpose. The amount of new wood added to a healthy tree during a year is very much greater than most people think. It is rather like a calculation in compound interest, for each twelve months the tree adds another "band" of wood to the outside of the trunk just beneath the bark, and every year the circumference is bigger so that the annual band of growth is progressively larger.

This rapid rate of accumulation of forest wealth means that there need be no danger of a timber famine if the producing countries look after their future output by afforestation and careful treatment of the young and growing trees. It is believed that much of the virgin timber of the European and American continents is approaching exhaustion (although very large reserves are available in Siberia), which makes it all the more important to see that every country does what it can to plant trees to yield usable timber. What should be done in this respect depends upon the soil and climatic conditions, the needs of industry and the size of the territory available. Canada and the United States need to maintain their Pacific Coast forests with the fine Douglas firs, hemlocks and silver spruces; Europe must keep up stocks of ordinary spruces, firs and larches.

The scientific approach to the question of the kinds of trees to grow may well be the most important branch of silviculture and forestry which future generations will have to study. Natural regeneration—if unregulated—means that there is little or no control over the trees that choose to scatter themselves across the countryside. Yet whether it be controlled regeneration or plantation production the needs of society must in the end exercise the final decision as to what is planted and reared. This may mean changes in the economic structure and outlook of whole regions, changes as shattering as any which follow major economic upheavals. Such a revolution was suggested by an American scientist recently, who pronounced the staggering theory that it would "pay" the Southern States of America to scrap their cotton production and grow trees instead, since cellulose, rayon, nylon and the rest of the twentieth century products had made cotton growing obsolete. He was arguing that cellulose and its derivatives are of the greatest significance to world society and, although cotton cellulose is the best available, it would be far more profitable from his country's point of view to grow timber for cellulose and thus take advantage not only of the higher yield of cellulose per acre planted, but also of the numerous by-products which timber would give. A great programme of research and enquiry would be necessary to prove the case; but that is not the most striking feature of the whole suggestion. Rather does its importance lie in the complete upheaval which would follow this novel employment of timber, for the Southern States, whose history has been interwoven like some rare fabric with the fortunes of cotton growing, would have to scrap the cotton plant and rear in its place plantations of trees. This is the kind of development which so alters the lives of men that it would be resisted violently by those to whom change is unwelcome; yet such resistance would not prevent the change but merely delay it until the clamours of the new became imperious or the opposition died silently away.

The casual approach to silvicultural problems has been superseded by the activities of the ecologist testing the soils to be planted, and choosing the environment; by the botanist selecting the species for rearing; by the entomologist dealing with the pests that can spoil good plantations; and by the forest pathologist diagnosing diseases and preventing their recurrence. The forestry expert watches over the growing trees and supervises their cutting and removal; it is then that the job of the utilisation expert begins. In this country, very little has been done to see that all these urgent jobs are carried through, although the Forestry Commission has tried to cover the whole ground with the limited resources at its disposal. Britain is not primarily a timber-producing country, and this deficiency has therefore not been attended by very serious consequences, except that much timber which would have been very useful in war time has been wantonly destroyed by neglect of these precautions. If the main problems were in future carefully studied there might be many successful forestry ventures; perhaps, for example, it would be found economically sound to plant large areas with trees suitable for pulping either for paper or for the extraction of cellulose for artificial silk. Other areas might prove very suitable plantations for some of the quicker growing softwoods such as larch, which would find a ready market for many purposes. The war-time development of the British plywood manufacturing industry suggests the growing of trees suitable for peeling into veneers, so that many of the higher grade plywoods previously imported from the Continent of Europe could be made in Britain, and compete effectively with the imported article. In this war, several home timbers have been used for plywood, and much more could have been done if in the past attention had been paid to developing in tree trunks the qualities particularly required for producing a good veneer.

These are the avenues of development which Britain should follow, since she will never be able to compete with Canada and the Soviet Union in the growing of sufficient quantities of ordinary softwoods or constructional timbers. There are specialised functions which Britain, with her high standards of scientific attainment and individual skill, could undertake and triumph as she has triumphed in days gone by. The mills of Lancashire used the raw materials brought from many thousands of miles and exported their fine textiles back again across the seven seas; and in more recent times precision engineering products, electrical goods and aeroplanes, mostly made from raw materials imported from other countries, have found markets in distant lands and in the face of extreme competition. After the war it will be necessary to turn Britain's resources to equally good account and in what may be called "intensive forestry production" there is an opportunity of achieving success.

Amongst the main world producers there is the certainty that every new discovery and invention in timber utilisation will mean a reduction in the costs of ordinary timber products. Thus the discovery of a means of using lignin in large quantities for industrial purposes would at once ease the problem of mill waste, sawdust, etc., and also aid paper manufacturers by giving them an outlet for what is now embarrassing waste. Changes, not only in the methods of production of the trees themselves, but also in all the ancillary processes such as sawmilling, planing and processing, seasoning, kiln drying and preservative treatment, can still further reduce the cost of the final product to industry and the consumer. The extent to which international collaboration in these matters has been pushed leaves much to be desired, and there will be numerous opportunities in the future for an extension of this co-operation.

One of the most profitable avenues of research has already been mentioned, the development of preservative methods and processes. These are designed not only to prevent the deterioration of timber in its various uses, but also to give to timber new features which it does not possess in its natural state and therefore add to its virtues. Here the growth of an even more close relationship between the timber and chemical industries promises to bring solid advantages to both of them; the former can say what it wants and the latter can provide the answer. Preservation is not, however, limited to preventing the destruction of the timber in its final form; there is, too, the need to limit the destruction of young and old trees by pests and fire. In the big producing areas such as the North American continent, the plague of fire has assumed alarming proportions, and special steps have had to be taken to prevent this enormous drain upon annual growth. It is in fact the main cause of serious loss and, although in this country it is naturally not such a menace, in the event of an extension of forest areas, all the experience of the Russians, Americans and Canadians would be valuable in preventing and controlling outbreaks. The activities of the pests of the nursery and woodland are of equal importance, and few can realise the really astounding quantity of timber which is lost to the world every year through these two causes. It was recently estimated officially that in the United States nearly half of the main lumber-producing areas were deficient in proper fire protection and could therefore be expected to yield well below the full product. The figures of fire losses in Canada are equally staggering, and one fire can destroy enough timber to keep the British market going for several weeks. The damage due to other causes may take the form of unhealthy trees being produced instead of healthy ones; yet the wastage cannot be very much smaller. The world could enjoy increased supplies of sawn timber and wood by-products if international collaboration enabled all producers to exchange up-to-date information on these vital topics.

The need for an extension of education and research has already been mentioned at some length; once the educational range has been widened the problem will be to utilise the trained personnel correctly. It will be futile to prepare many young men as experts in forestry or timber utilisation only to find that the industry still maintains its old ideas and methods of trading. These new men must meet a definite need—the need for highly qualified experts in every branch of the industry, who are recognised as experts and remunerated according to a professional standard. They cannot be forced upon an unwilling industry. The status of forestry and similar studies in the University curriculum must be raised, and Oxford University has recently taken the excellent step of making forestry a major subject of post-graduate work. The greatest development will come when, as with other industries, such as metallurgy, the industry itself realises the importance of highly trained personnel, and establishes full contact with the educational bodies so that both support and financial aid are readily forthcoming. The timber technicians of the future must be just as highly qualified as the chemists, engineers and architects. The belief that in the timber trade, experience begins and ends in the market square may have been an adequate one in the nineteenth century; today it is hopelessly out of date.

No imaginative approach to the technical side of the timber industry is of very much good unless at the same time the economics of this ancient trade are fully understood. In the early days, trees were looked upon in the same way as minerals—they were discovered, exploited and the exploiters moved on to other areas to begin the same process all over again. In other words, there was no attempt to treat timber as a crop to be cut, planted, tended and developed. No one would think of mowing a field of corn when the ears were green and half-formed; yet even today, many woodland owners will sell their trees irrespective of the state of their maturity. Trees have a life after which they are "ripe" or mature in the same way as crops and to maximise the economic advantage of tree production, cutting should in general only be carried out at this optimum time. It is when the tree is fully mature that it contains the most useful quantity of timber; to cut it at fifty years of age instead of its mature age of perhaps sixty is to lose very much more than one-fifth of the possible timber, for during those last ten years the tree would probably have put on as much useful timber as in the fifteen or twenty years previously.

Timber has this very important advantage over practically every other basic raw material—it can be regenerated at a rapid rate if the most elementary precautions are taken. It is essential to the economic stability of timber production that this fact be recognised, and all who plant must be encouraged to plan for a sustained yield. In some of the main producing countries, forest owners have formed "tree banks", a system which aims not only to give owners a regular monetary return from the felling of their trees but also ensures that no tree is cut before it is fully mature. The owner, who is not perhaps a timber expert, will "deposit" the wood or plantation with the "bankers"; they survey the trees, ascertain the approximate average age by cutting down one or two of the larger trees, and calculate what percentage of the plantation should be cut every year in order to give a fixed return and also maintain intact the capital value of the plantation. The tree bank will, of course, make payments in advance to needy depositors, but they will not fell in excess of the permitted percentage. The capital value of such "banked" plantations far exceeds the price which could be obtained in the open market for slashing the whole plantation clean at one operation. It has the further advantage that the bank will only cut the mature trees, whereas the sawmiller who purchases a whole plantation will probably clean the site of all trees, using the smaller ones for poles and props; he cannot afford to select the best trees suitable for cutting and save the others. In addition he will not replant where he has cut, but will wish to sell the site for other purposes or allow it to become derelict from the timber point of view until he can find a real estate buyer.

Another important feature of timber production is that the cost of acquiring the round logs is but a small part of the final price of timber ready for the consumer's use. Before the log can be cut, a great deal of money in labour and transport charges will have been expended; and later on, after it has passed through the mill, transport once again bulks large. In the case of the timber imported into this country, some species are hauled for such long distances by land and sea that the price to the importer is more than half transport charges. Even the home-produced timber prices are probably about one-third such charges, so that the development of a healthy industry is dependent upon the provision of cheap and efficient transport and a great deal of specialised equipment. Since according to import figures, timber proves to be one of the imports with the lowest value *per ton*, the need for reasonable freight charges is manifest.

The vital change which has taken place in timber production is that it has now acquired a cost of production which is not just the charges incurred in felling and sawing. In the past its economic cost was of a nature similar to that of coal or iron ore, and depended upon the quantity available at any one point and how accessible that quantity was. When the virgin falls were exhausted, the sawmiller would move off to a less easily exploited spot and his costs would be that much higher, in the same way as the coal owner must burrow deeper as the seam gets less productive. Today, the cost of timber is dependent upon a different series of costs—the costs of planting, nursing and rearing a plantation for a number of years, with the resulting tie up of capital resources over a long period. A modern economic system need not regard this extended period of production as presenting any difficulties if those who cannot undertake the necessary waiting are helped along, since it is better for society to aid them in this manner than that they should be forced to cut before the trees are fully mature. To do so would be to lose for ever a certain percentage of the annual crop.

*   *   *   *   *   *

What will happen to Britain's timber supplies at the end of the Second World War? It is dangerous to indulge in prophecy, yet a few trends can be discerned which will condition the extent and status of the post-war timber industry. Britain will most certainly need very large quantities of timber to make good the destruction which has been wrought by German bombs and to rebuild her industries which have been changed over to meet the demands of war. Therefore it will be necessary and wise to maintain some of the controls which exist today to ensure that the Government stocks which will probably be available at the end are disposed of without the period of wild speculation which followed the 1914-1918 War. Very few persons can be said to have benefited from this period of speculation and rocketing prices, and they were not the ordinary users of timber. With the experience of the war, it should not be difficult to devise a scheme which, although it reflects the desire of many for a remission of some of the more stringent controls of war time, nevertheless prevents a wild inflation of prices for the benefit of a very few. The houses of the people and their daily wants are too important to be left to the unsteady influence of the "market" and fixed "ceiling" prices should prevent the worst abuses.

To estimate what Britain will do about her huge volume of timber imports is difficult. It seems clear, however, that in view of the necessity of regulating the external value of the pound, it will be essential to ration supplies of foreign exchange by allocating amounts to the various raw material purchasing bodies. Timber and timber goods varied from 5 to 10 per cent. of the total value of imports in peace time, and an import of this magnitude can only be maintained in the new circumstances if it bears the proper relation to the needs of other industries. On the other hand, there is the possibility of developing some branches of timber production—such as plywood manufacture—into flourishing export industries which will incidentally give them a clearer claim to the import of raw material. This development must take time, and will depend to a very large extent upon the rôle that Britain chooses to assume in the world economy. In any event, timber is likely to find itself allocated a limited amount of purchasing power to be expended in certain designated countries; States, that is to say, with which Britain wishes to establish a close trading relationship. Since many producing countries will only slowly return to their normal place as world timber exporters, these restrictions are unlikely to be as drastic as they sound today.

In spite of these difficulties, the timber industry has a very real chance of achieving a major contribution to the industrial future of the country. What remains of home resources can be adequately organised to yield the maximum product and plans prepared to ensure a supply of trees suitable for future needs. Here the importance of the new Government plans for forestry must be emphasised, since everyone concerned awaits with the greatest interest the lead which the Government can give in replanting Britain's trees at the earliest possible moment. Secondly, every effort should be made to ensure that all the waste and by-products emerging from forestry operations and timber conversion are used to produce other industrial products. With the war-time shortage of labour relieved and evidence of a less conservative policy on the part of the banks, new industrial ventures may be launched to develop from the tree trunk the many products that lurk there.

No one can see into the future, but it is safe to say that once the major possibilities of timber utilisation have been grasped and the important war-time inventions disclosed, a wide road lies ahead. An absorbing task awaits those who are able and willing to grow the trees correctly, and to use the many products that the tree will yield as the means of bettering the material equipment of human society.

CHISWICK PRESS